Edexcel GCSE (9–1)
Combined Science
Homework and skills Higher

Some of the questions help you to develop different skills, shown by the icons below.

 Maths skills

 Knowledge and understanding of practicals

 Reading and writing skills

 Research skills

Published by Pearson Education Limited, 80 Strand, London, WC2R 0RL.

www.pearsonschoolsandfecolleges.co.uk

Text and illustrations © Pearson Education Limited

Typeset by Phoenix Photosetting, Kent

Cover design by Peter Stratton

The rights of Mark Levesley, Penny Johnson, Sue Kearsey, Iain Brand, Nigel Saunders, Sue Robilliard to be identified as authors of this work have been asserted by them in accordance with the Copyright, Designs and Patents Act 1988.

The Publishers would like to thank the following people for their contribution to the text: John Kavanagh, Carol Tear, John Ling, Mary Jones, James de Winter and Miles Hudson.

First published 2018

21 20 19 18

10 9 8 7 6 5 4 3 2

ISBN: 978 1 292 24711 3

Printed by Neografia

Cover image: Science Photo Library Ltd: NASA

All other media © Pearson Education

Pearson Education Limited is not responsible for the content of any external internet sites. It is essential for tutors to preview each website before using it in class so as to ensure that the URL is still accurate, relevant and appropriate. We suggest that tutors bookmark useful websites and consider enabling students to access them through the school/college intranet.

A note from the Publishers: Pearson Education Limited: This resource is based on the March 2016 accredited version of the specification. The homework activities in this resource have not been reviewed or endorsed by Edexcel and should not be considered as being published by Edexcel.

Copies of official specifications for all Edexcel qualifications may be found on the website: www.edexcel.com

While the Publishers have made every attempt to ensure that advice on the qualification and its assessment is accurate, the official specification and associated assessment guidance materials are the only authoritative source of information and should always be referred to for definitive guidance. Pearson examiners have not contributed to any sections in this resource relevant to examination papers for which they have responsibility. Examiners will not use this resource as a source of material for any assessment set by Pearson.

The homework activities are not required to achieve this Pearson qualification. It is not the only suitable material available to support the qualification, and any resource lists produced by the awarding body shall include appropriate resources.

1. Complete the table to show the missing magnifications.

Eyepiece lens magnification	Objective lens magnification	Total magnification
×3	×5	
	×10	×60
×7.5		×225
	×20	×250

2. A red blood cell is 8 μm in diameter. How big will its diameter be if magnified ×2000? Show your working and give your answer in millimetres.

3. The diagram shows what happens inside an electron microscope.

a beam of electrons is generated

air molecules interfere with electron beam and so there is a vacuum inside the instrument

a. What goes through a specimen in a school microscope to create an image?

the electron beam is made into a finer, more powerful beam using an electromagnetic coil

another electromagnetic coil directs the electron beam onto a part of the specimen

b. Which of the three electromagnetic coils is most like the objective lens on a school microscope? Explain your reasoning.

preparing the specimen is a complicated and time-consuming process in which the specimen is cut extremely thinly and placed on a mesh

the electron beam goes through the specimen, creating an image

another electromagnetic coil magnifies the image

the image becomes visible when it hits a screen, and a black-and-white image can be obtained

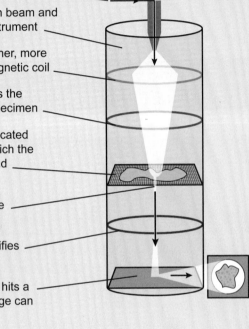

c. Explain why an electron microscope would not be used to watch the heart of a water flea pumping.

d. Explain why an electron microscope would not be used to examine the dots of colour used to produce photographs in a newspaper.

e. Explain why an electron microscope would be used to see the details in the cytoplasm of a cell.

1. a. What is an estimate?_____

b. Why do we use estimates?_____

_____

c. When can an estimate be used and when can it not?_____

_____

_____

2. The cell below is one of the following: oak leaf cell, human liver cell, human eye (retina) cell, onion bulb cell, cat skin cell.

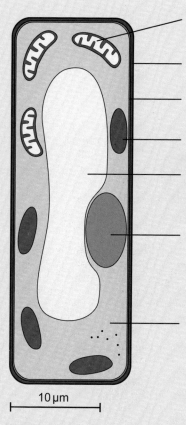

10 µm

a. Which type of cell is it? Explain your reasoning.

_____

_____

_____

b. Label the sub-cellular parts of the cell on the diagram, together with a description of each part's function.

3. The image to the right shows the view through a microscope when looking at a special type of slide with a fine scale on it. What is the diameter of the **field of view**?

_____

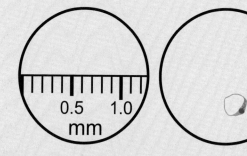

1. Look at the drawings below. Decide whether each of the cells is **prokaryotic** or **eukaryotic**. Explain your reasoning for each one.

A

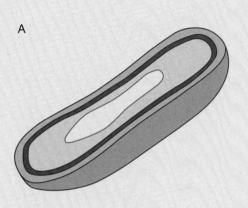

B

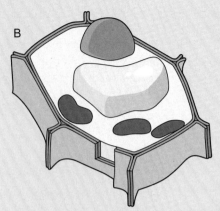

C

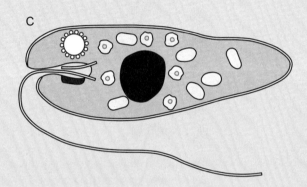

D

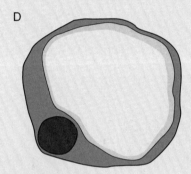

2. A bacterial ribosome is 20 nm in diameter.

a. Write this diameter in metres. Give your answer as an ordinary number.

_____

b. Give your answer to part **a** in standard form.

_____

H **c.** One bacterial ribosome is magnified 2×10^6 times. Calculate its magnified diameter in metres.

_____

H **3.** A bacterium that is 3.5×10^{-6} m long appears in a micrograph as 7×10^{-2} m long. Calculate the magnification of the micrograph.

Plants absorb water and dissolved mineral salts from the soil through their roots. The roots have cells called root hair cells which are specialised for absorption. The water and mineral salts move through other cells in the roots until they enter long tubes called xylem vessels. Once in the xylem they can travel to all other parts of the plant.

1. Name and describe the transport process by which water molecules are absorbed by a root hair cell from the soil.

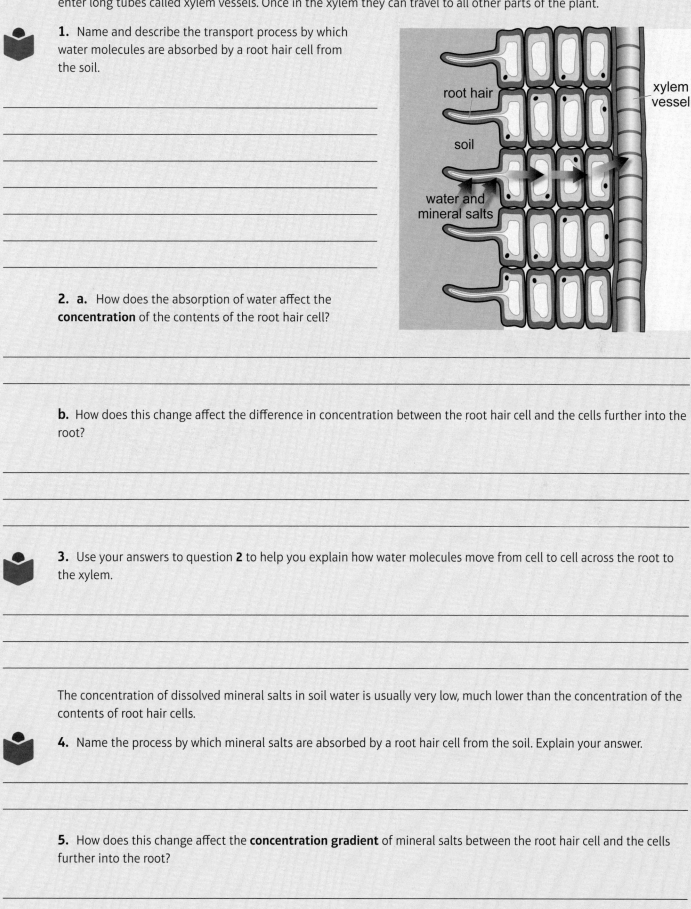

root hair

xylem vessel

soil

water and mineral salts

_____

_____

_____

_____

_____

_____

_____

2. a. How does the absorption of water affect the **concentration** of the contents of the root hair cell?

_____

_____

b. How does this change affect the difference in concentration between the root hair cell and the cells further into the root?

_____

_____

_____

3. Use your answers to question **2** to help you explain how water molecules move from cell to cell across the root to the xylem.

_____

_____

_____

The concentration of dissolved mineral salts in soil water is usually very low, much lower than the concentration of the contents of root hair cells.

4. Name the process by which mineral salts are absorbed by a root hair cell from the soil. Explain your answer.

_____

_____

5. How does this change affect the **concentration gradient** of mineral salts between the root hair cell and the cells further into the root?

_____

_____

Sciences **CB2a** Mitosis
Homework & skills

1. State **two** processes that take place during **interphase**.

_____

_____

2. The stages of **mitosis** are **prophase**, **metaphase**, **anaphase**, **telophase** and **cytokinesis**. Write a brief description of what happens in each stage.

_____

_____

_____

_____

_____

_____

_____

_____

3. A student writes this in an exam: 'Mitosis is important for growth and repair but not for **asexual reproduction**.'

Explain whether you agree with each part of this statement or not.

_____

_____

_____

_____

_____

_____

4. The cells produced from mitosis are genetically identical **diploid** cells.

a. Describe how the cell produces genetically identical **daughter cells**.

_____

_____

b. Describe what 'diploid' means.

_____

_____

c. Explain why most cells in the body need to be diploid.

_____

_____

_____

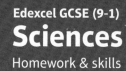

Sciences
CB2c Growth in plants
Homework & skills

1. Vascular cambium is a type of plant **meristem**. Explain what this means.

_____

_____

2. Name the process by which cells produced from cambium cells become **xylem cells**.

_____

_____

3. Describe the special features of xylem vessels made from xylem cells, and explain how these features allow the xylem to be adapted to its function.

_____

_____

_____

_____

_____

_____

_____

_____

_____

_____

_____

_____

Scientists are studying the growth of young trees to see if the predicted increase in atmospheric carbon dioxide concentrations will have an impact. The table below shows the results from a study that measured the dry mass of different parts of spruce tree seedlings growing in different carbon dioxide concentrations.

Carbon dioxide concentration	Dry mass at 30 days (mg)			Dry mass at 100 days (mg)		
	root	stem	leaf	root	stem	leaf
normal atmospheric	0.005	0.001	0.009	0.298	0.069	0.595
high	0.009	0.002	0.015	0.428	0.069	0.656

4. Calculate the percentage gain in mass of **roots** between 30 and 100 days in normal and high carbon dioxide concentrations.

_____

Inside all your muscles are muscle spindles that contain receptor cells. The muscle spindles are stretched when a muscle is stretched. When this happens an impulse is generated, which is sent along a sensory neurone. The impulse is transmitted through a **reflex arc**, causing the muscle to contract (or contract even more).

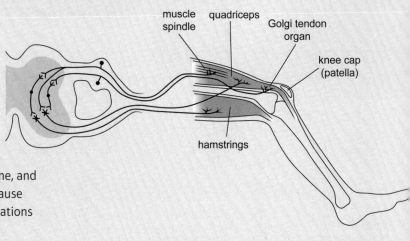

Even if you are standing still, minute variations in position are occurring all the time, and these are detected by muscle spindles and cause **reflexes** that automatically make slight alterations to muscle tensions, so that you stay upright.

The knee jerk reflex (or patellar reflex) is one of these reflexes and it occurs using a monosynaptic (single synapse) reflex arc. However, it is not quite as simple as that!

Another sensory neurone runs from a receptor called the Golgi tendon organ. As the quadriceps muscle contracts, it pulls on the tendon and stretches it. If the quadriceps muscle contracts too much, and there is a danger that the tendon could be damaged, the Golgi tendon organ sends impulses to a **relay neurone**, which connects to the **motor neurone** going to the quadriceps. This relay neurone uses a **neurotransmitter** called glycine in its **synapse** with the motor neurone, and this inhibits (decreases the chances of) an impulse being generated in the motor neurone. Most synapses use a neurotransmitter called acetylcholine (ACh) that stimulates (increases the chances of) impulses being generated.

1. a. What is meant by the term 'monosynaptic reflex arc'?

_____

b. State a purpose of reflex arcs.

_____

c. Explain what happens at a synapse.

_____

_____

_____

_____

d. State **one** drawback of synapses in the nervous system.

_____

e. State **one** benefit of synapses in the nervous system.

_____

2. a. What is the effect on the quadriceps muscle when the tendon is stretched too much?

_____

b. Why is this useful?

_____

c. Weightlifters have been known to inject themselves with local anaesthetic near their Golgi tendon organs. Why do you think they do this?

_____

_____

_____

Sciences CB3a Meiosis
Homework & skills

1. A body cell contains a person's genome. Define the term 'genome'.

_____

_____

2. A protein is a polymer.

a. State what is meant by 'polymer'.

_____

b. Describe the basic structure of all proteins.

_____

c. Where are the instructions for making a protein stored?

_____

d. What part of a cell manufactures proteins?

_____

3. Look at the diagram below. It shows two forms of cell division.

 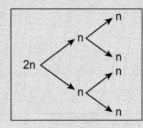

a. Explain what the diagram shows, in terms of the differences between the two processes.

_____

_____

_____

_____

_____

_____

_____

_____

_____

_____

_____

b. Describe **one** situation in which each process is used.

_____

_____

_____

_____

_____

1. Look at the genetic diagram below. It shows the monohybrid inheritance of a flower colour gene. The allele B causes blue flowers and the allele b causes white flowers.

	Parent 1	Parent 2
genotypes of parents	BB	Bb
possible gametes	◯ ◯	◯ ◯
possible offspring genotypes	▢ ▢	▢ ▢
possible offspring phenotypes	▭ ▭	▭ ▭

a. Complete the diagram.

b. Which of the parent plants was homozygous? _____

c. What percentage of the offspring plants would you expect to be heterozygous? _____

d. What is the phenotype of parent 1? _____

e. What is the phenotype of parent 2? _____

f. Explain why there is only one phenotype in the offspring plants.

_____

_____

2. Eating asparagus often makes people's urine smell because sulfur compounds are excreted. The allele for excreting sulfur compounds after eating asparagus is dominant (A). The allele for non-smelly urine is a.

Kevin's urine does not smell after eating asparagus. His wife, Jackie, does have smelly urine. They have five children, two of whom have non-smelly urine. Work out Jackie's genotype for this allele.

3. Many pea plants have rounded pods, but some have flat pods because they are homozygous for a recessive allele (d). A plant that is homozygous for the dominant allele and another plant that has flat pods are crossed. Two of the offspring are then taken and they are crossed to produce more offspring (called F2 offspring). There are 200 F2 offspring plants. Predict the number that will have flat pods. Show all your working.

Sciences

CB3e Gene mutation

The techniques developed during the Human Genome Project (HGP) have helped to identify over 1800 disease-related genes. These techniques have been improved so they are now far quicker and cheaper to do than when the project started. This has made it possible to analyse many genomes and look for variation within the genes related to disease.

Two genes that are related to breast cancer were identified before the HGP was completed. These are the *BRCA1* and *BRCA2* genes. Both genes produce proteins: BRCA1 and BRCA2 – shown in upright letters to distinguish the protein from the gene. These proteins normally help repair damaged DNA, particularly in breast tissue. Damaged cells are more likely to develop into cancers than healthy cells are. Breast cancer can occur in men as well as women, although women are at greater risk as they have many more breast cells than men.

Many differences have been found in these genes between different people. Some differences are the result of one or more changes to the DNA base pairs in the gene. Certain variations affect the risk of developing breast cancer, as shown in the table.

	Proportion of woman having breast cancer before age 80		Bases in the relevant section of DNA code	
	BRCA1	BRCA2	BRCA1	BRCA2
normal allele	12%	12%	CAGTGTCCT	TCTATATTC
allele X	12%	12%	CAGTGCCCT	TCTATCTTC
allele Y	60–90%	45–85%	CAGAGTCCT	TCTACATTC

Women with breast cancer receive a range of treatments, including drugs. Herceptin is a drug that targets cancer cells that are producing a lot of the HER2 protein. These kinds of cancer cells are found in about 15–30 per cent of breast cancers. Herceptin is not only very expensive, it can also be poisonous to heart cells.

1. Describe the main aim of the Human Genome Project.

_____

_____

2. a. Which name is given to the process that produces a new allele of a gene?   _____

b. When does this process usually happen?

_____

_____

c. Use evidence from the table to identify how alleles X and Y for each gene have changed from the normal (most common) version.

_____

_____

_____

_____

3. Explain how the normal alleles of the *BRCA1* and *BRCA2* genes help to prevent the development of breast cancer.

_____

_____

_____

_____

In October 2004, scientists excavating a cave on the island of Flores in Indonesia discovered an almost whole skeleton of a human-like **species**. These bones were dated to 18 000 years old, but were of an individual that was only about the size of a normal three-year-old. By looking at the bones carefully, the scientists could tell that the bones had stopped growing and the skeleton was that of an adult. It became known as the 'Hobbit' human, from the small hobbit people in Tolkien's *Lord of the Rings*.

Other excavations on neighbouring islands have shown that *Homo erectus* lived in the area, and that the first signs of *Homo sapiens* in the region were 40 000 years ago.

1. State **two** different possible explanations for what the human-like species could have been.

_____

_____

_____

_____

_____

Comparing the skull of the new 'Hobbit' human fossil with *Homo erectus* and *Homo sapiens* skulls, the scientists who found the skeleton decided that they had found a new human-like species that had evolved from *Homo erectus*. They called this new species *Homo floresiensis*. They were not surprised that the skeleton was small, because species that evolve on islands are often very different in size from the species on the mainland from which they evolved. Alongside the tiny human were bones of a very small elephant species (a pygmy species) and giant-sized lizards and rats.

The scientists also found stone tools in the same cave. Many were primitive stone flakes, but a few (found next to an elephant skeleton) were more complex, including spear blades. These tools were difficult to date. Evidence of burning of bones suggested that some of the elephant meat had been cooked for food.

2. What does the evidence of the tools and burning suggest about *Homo floresiensis*?

_____

_____

_____

3. Many other scientists have not accepted the idea of a new human species. The biggest problem they have is that the brain size of the individual found is smaller than that of *Homo erectus* or *Homo sapiens*, even for its body size. The simplest explanation is that this human was suffering from a type of condition that stopped it growing normally.

a. What does brain size suggest about intelligence?

_____

_____

_____

b. What does the evidence of the brain size suggest about the tools found in the cave?

_____

_____

_____

Here is some information about three **kingdoms** into which organisms are classified. You are not expected to remember all this information.

Fungi	Prokaryotes	Protists
• cells have cell walls made of chitin • cells have nuclei • cannot make their own food • smallest are yeast cells, which are about 0.01 mm in diameter	• very simple and single-celled • cells do not have nuclei • most have cell walls that contain peptidoglycan • smallest are about 0.0003 mm in diameter, and largest are 0.6 mm in diameter	• some are single-celled, and some have more than one cell • some can photosynthesise • cells have nuclei • many do not have cell walls • smallest are about 0.002 mm in diameter, and largest are about 65 m long

1. a. Name **two** other kingdoms.

b. Describe **one** feature of the organisms found in each of these other two kingdoms.

2. Explain the **best** way to tell the difference between a single-celled protist and a prokaryote.

3. Some scientists have discovered what they think are the fossils of organisms in some meteorites that contain rock from Mars. The fossils look like a row of single cells, with diameters of about 0.1 μm.
If these are fossilised organisms, which kingdom are they most likely to have belonged to? Explain your reasoning.

4. Moles are mammals that live underground. The golden mole of southern Africa and the marsupial mole of Australia are very similar-looking animals and were thought to be closely related. They both have cone-shaped heads, short legs with powerful claws, non-functioning eyes that are covered with skin, and a leathery pad to cover and protect their nostrils. However, new research has confirmed that they are not related at all, apart from both being mammals.

a. Why were golden moles and marsupial moles originally placed in a group of closely related animals?

b. Suggest which new research has confirmed that they are not closely related.

c. Suggest why the two animals have ended up looking so much like one another.

1. Rare breeds of farm animal are often kept on rare-breed farms. Seeds from rare varieties of plants are stored in gene banks. Give **one** reason why plant varieties and animal breeds are preserved in this way.

_____

 H 2. The table shows some different enzymes that are used to cut DNA.

Enzyme	Where it cuts DNA
BamHI	G GATCC
	CCTAG G
EcoRI	G AATTC
	CTTAA G
HpaI	GTTA AC
	CAAT TG
PstI	CTGCA G
	G ACGTC
TaqI	T CGA
	AGCT

a. What name is given to this type of enzyme?

_____

b. Explain which enzyme would be least suitable for use in making recombinant DNA.

_____

_____

c. Explain why the same enzyme is used to cut out the gene of interest and to cut the plasmid into which the gene is to be inserted.

_____

_____

_____

d. Draw a diagram to show how a bacterium could be genetically engineered to produce human growth hormone.

e. Give **one** advantage of producing human growth hormone in this way.

_____

_____

f. Suggest **one** possible disadvantage.

_____

_____

Edexcel GCSE (9-1)

Sciences **CB5a** Health and disease

Homework & skills

CB5 Health, Disease
and the Development
of Medicines

The table below shows life expectancy for men and average household wealth for different regions of England.

	Life expectancy of men (years)	Average total household wealth (£)
North East	78.0	142 700
North West	78.1	179 100
Yorkshire and The Humber	78.7	184 200
East Midlands	79.4	207 200
West Midlands	78.9	186 800
East	80.4	259 900
London	80.3	213 200
South East	80.5	309 700
South West	80.2	288 300

1. a What is meant by a **correlation**?

_____

_____

b. A good way of looking for correlations is to draw scatter diagrams (scatter graphs). Use the data in the table to draw a scatter graph of life expectancy against wealth.

c. Does your scatter graph suggest a correlation between these factors? If so, describe it.

_____

_____

d. Suggest **two** reasons for any correlation shown in your scatter graph.

_____

_____

Recent advice on reducing the risk of **cardiovascular disease** compares people who are apple shaped (most fat around the waist) with those who are pear shaped (more fat around the hips than waist). Fat around the hips is mostly just beneath the skin (subcutaneous), while fat around the waist is often inside the body cavity around the organs (visceral).

One study recorded how many people within a group of 972 **obese** patients had cardiovascular disease during a period of eight years. The number was converted to a value of risk of cardiovascular disease and compared with the position of fat, as measured using X-rays and MRI scans. The group was split into four quartiles for each position of fat. Quartile 1 shows people with the lowest amount of fat, and quartile 4 the largest.

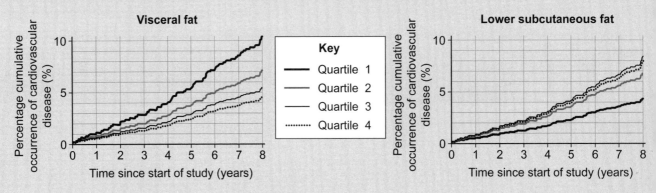

How position of body fat in obese people affects the proportion who develop cardiovascular disease.

1. Simple measures of body fat are **body mass index (BMI)** and **waist : hip (waist to hip) ratio**. Describe how each of these measures is calculated.

_____

_____

_____

_____

_____

2. Two obese people of the same height have identical masses, but one is apple shaped and one is pear shaped. Suggest how their BMI and waist : hip ratios compare.

_____

_____

_____

_____

3. Use the charts to draw a conclusion about how the risk of cardiovascular disease is affected by the:

a. amount of visceral fat

_____

_____

_____

b. amount of subcutaneous fat.

_____

_____

Plasmodium, the protist that causes malaria, is spread by *Anopheles* mosquitoes. These mosquitoes are most commonly found in tropical countries. Female mosquitoes feed on blood, including that of humans, to provide nutrients for their eggs. At other times they feed on nectar and plant juices, as do male mosquitoes. Fertilised mosquito eggs are laid in water, where the young hatch and live for a few weeks. They then develop into flying adults, which may live for between a week and several months.

1. What name is given to animals, such as mosquitoes, that transmit infection?

_____

2. Sketch a life cycle for the mosquito.

3. Describe **one** advantage for *Plasmodium* of being spread by mosquitoes.

_____

_____

Malaria kills more people than any other disease. In 2010 there were an estimated 219 million cases, resulting in about 660 000 deaths. Protist cells are similar to human cells, so medicines that harm *Plasmodium* can also harm people, particularly if used over a long time. Therefore, many attempts to control malaria focus on controlling mosquitoes.

During the 20th century, insecticides (chemicals that kill insects) were sprayed over water and land to kill *Anopheles* mosquitoes. However, many mosquitoes developed resistance to the insecticides. The chemicals also caused damage to the environment by killing other organisms. Use of the chemicals is now mainly restricted to surfaces in homes, or nets placed around people when they sleep. Water tanks are kept covered and pools and puddles treated to kill young mosquitoes.

4. Explain why control of malaria is not only focused on killing *Plasmodium*.

_____

_____

_____

_____

5. Explain why controlling mosquitoes should help to control the spread of malaria.

_____

_____

_____

_____

_____

A national **screening** programme for *Chlamydia* infection in under-25s began in the UK in 2003. It is a free service, intended to encourage young people to avoid infection or, if they become infected, to help them get treatment quickly. There may be no early signs of *Chlamydia* infection, although some people suffer pain when urinating or have an unusual discharge. Long-term infection can cause more severe problems, including becoming sterile (unable to have children). Infection can be treated simply with antibiotics.

1. a. To which group of infections does *Chlamydia* belong?

_____

b. Describe **two** ways in which the pathogen that causes *Chlamydia* is spread.

_____

_____

c. Name **one** other pathogen that is spread in a similar way.

_____

Pathogens like *Chlamydia* use human behaviour to bypass many of the barriers and defences of the human body that protect it against infection.

2. State **two physical barriers** of the human body to infection, and explain how they work.

_____

_____

_____

The chart shows the percentage of men and women of different age groups who were diagnosed with *Chlamydia* infection in 2013 in England.

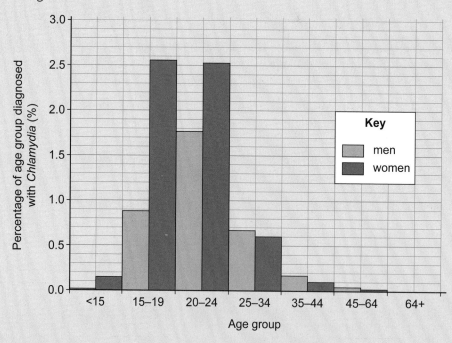

Percentage of men and women in England in 2013 diagnosed with **Chlamydia** *by age group.*

3. Which age groups of males and of females show the highest proportion of *Chlamydia* infections?

_____

4. Suggest **two** reasons why these age groups are more at risk of infection with *Chlamydia* than others.

_____

_____

Teixobactin is a new **antibiotic** discovered in 2015. It was the first antibiotic to be discovered for around 30 years. Extracts from soil bacteria had shown that the species *Eleftheria terrae* contained an antibiotic substance. This substance was effective against several pathogens of humans, including *Mycobacterium tuberculosis*. However, this bacterium could not be grown in a lab and so a new technique had to be developed so that the bacterial cells could be grown in pure cultures (cultures that contain only one bacterial species) in the soil. The antibiotic purified from *Eleftheria* was called teixobactin.

Teixobactin works by binding to a lipid molecule that some kinds of bacteria use to make their cell walls. The binding prevents the bacterium from using the lipids, so the cell wall is weakened. Osmosis into the cell causes the bacterial cell membrane to burst. Teixobactin is the first antibiotic to be developed that affects lipids. Other antibiotics usually act against proteins. Scientists hope that the way teixobactin works will reduce the risk of bacteria developing resistance to it, as they have to other antibiotics.

Clinical trials of teixobactin are unlikely to happen before 2018. Those will take another two to three years, and the total cost of development, if the antibiotic is successful, will be more than £50 million. It is uncertain yet whether any drug company will want to spend this amount to complete the testing, as they will not earn money from the drug until it is used by doctors.

1. Explain what is meant by antibiotic.

_____

_____

2. Explain why *Eleftheria terrae* is difficult to grow in culture.

_____

3. Explain the role of osmosis in the antibiotic effect of teixobactin.

_____

_____

_____

4. Explain why teixobactin should be safe to use in human cells.

_____

_____

5. **Pre-clinical testing** of teixobactin has been done on infected human cells. Describe the remaining stages of testing that are needed before the new antibiotic can be licensed for use by doctors. Explain why each of the stages is carried out.

_____

_____

_____

_____

_____

_____

_____

_____

Edexcel GCSE (9-1)

Sciences
Homework & skills

CB6b Factors that affect
photosynthesis

CB6 Plant Structures and
their Functions

1. Bottles of algae in pH indicator solution were placed at different distances from a lamp. The pH in each bottle at the start was 8.4. The pH values after an hour are shown in the table.

Tube	A	B	C	D	E
pH after one hour	8.4	9.1	8.6	8.8	9.0

Suggest which tube was closest to the lamp. Explain your answer.

_____

_____

_____

_____

2. The graph shows how the **rate** of photosynthesis changes in some pondweed as the light intensity increases.

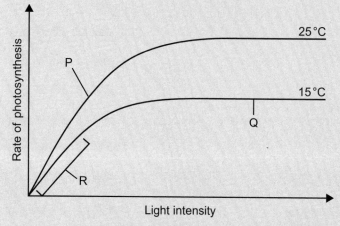

a. Look at the slope labelled R. What does this line tell you about the relationship between light intensity and the rate of photosynthesis?

_____

_____

b. Define the term '**limiting factor**'.

_____

c. What is the limiting factor at point P?

_____

d. Why can the factor in **c** limit photosynthesis?

_____

_____

e. What is the limiting factor at point Q on the graph?

_____

f. Why can the factor in **e** be limiting for photosynthesis?

_____

_____

g. State one other limiting factor of photosynthesis.

_____

1. A student carries out an experiment using the **potometer** shown and an electric fan, which is set at different powers.

The results are shown in the table below.

Fan power setting (W)	Distance moved by bubble in five minutes (mm)		
	Trial 1	Trial 2	Trial 3
10	22	27	26
15	35	36	34
20	42	44	49
25	55	55	56

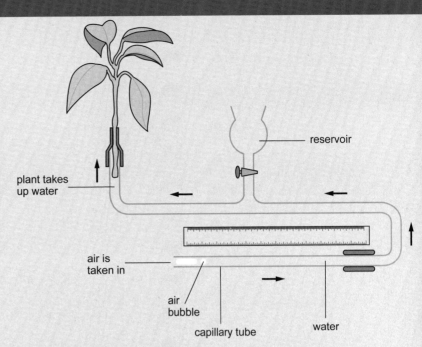

a. Calculate the mean values of the repeated readings.

_____

b. Calculate the mean rate of **transpiration** for each power setting.

_____

c. Draw a graph to show the linear relationship between the fan power and the rate of transpiration.

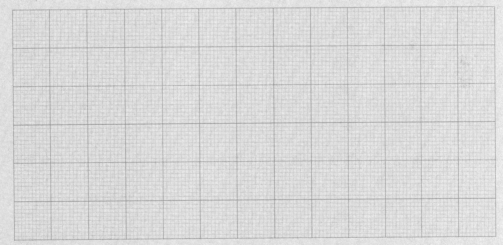

2. The linear relationship shown by the line of best fit can be represented as $y = mx + c$.

a. Calculate the slope (gradient) of the line (m).

_____

b. What is the value of c, the y-intercept? This will give you an estimation of the rate of transpiration without air movement.

_____

_____

The responses of the body to stimuli (changes internally and externally) may be controlled by the nervous system or **hormonal system**, or sometimes both systems. Each system has particular features.

1. Give the general name for glands that produce **hormones**.

_____

_____

2. State **one** hormone that is produced by each of these glands.

a. adrenal gland _____

b. testes _____

c. thyroid gland _____

3. State the location of the gland that produces each of these hormones.

a. oestrogen _____

b. insulin _____

c. growth hormone _____

4. Draw a table with one column to display features of the nervous system, and one column to display features of the hormonal system. Add five rows to your table, to cover the following features.

  i how a stimulus is detected

  ii how information is transmitted around the body

  iii speed of transmission

  iv duration of effect

  v number of potential response sites.

Complete the table for each system.

5. Use your table to help you explain why we have two different control systems.

_____

_____

_____

_____

H 1. Complete the sentences to explain why these hormonal changes occur in the menstrual cycle.

a. The concentration of **FSH** rises after menstruation because ...

_____

_____

_____

b. Oestrogen concentration increases in the first half of the cycle because ...

_____

_____

_____

c. The concentration of **LH** rises to a peak just before ovulation because ...

_____

_____

_____

d. The concentration of progesterone increases in the second half of the cycle because ...

_____

_____

Clomifene therapy is one form of **Assisted Reproductive Technology (ART)**, used with women who rarely or never ovulate.

H 2. What is the aim of ART?

_____

_____

H 3. a. Explain how clomifene therapy affects some of the hormones that control the menstrual cycle.

_____

_____

_____

H b. Explain how the effect you describe in **a** can increase the chance of pregnancy.

_____

_____

_____

H 4. Clomifene therapy is given at a particular stage of the menstrual cycle. Suggest, with a reason, when this stage is.

_____

_____

_____

_____

Studies have shown that some fat cells release hormone-like substances into the blood that cause liver cells and muscle cells to become more resistant to insulin. The fat cells that do this are found more in fatty tissue in the abdomen (abdominal or visceral fat). This fat surrounds major organs such as the heart, liver and kidneys. Fat that is found just below the skin (subcutaneous fat) is less likely to produce the hormone-like substances.

1. a. Suggest, with reasons, **two** tissues that can contribute to an increase in body mass in an adult's body. (*Hint:* think of different activities that can increase the mass of particular tissues.)

_____

_____

b. Average adult body mass in the UK is increasing. This increase correlates with an increase in the proportion of adults with **type 2 diabetes**. Use the information above to suggest a cause of this.

_____

_____

2. a. The equation for calculating **body mass index (BMI)** is $\dfrac{\text{weight (kg)}}{(\text{height (m)})^2}$.

Describe how BMI changes as an adult increases in body mass.

_____

b. Explain why type 2 diabetes shows a better correlation with BMI than with body mass.

_____

_____

Accurate measurement of the mass of body fat is not easy and requires special equipment. Health professionals are looking for the best simple measurement to use, so they can more easily and accurately assess a person's risk of developing conditions such as type 2 diabetes.

3. Using your answer to question **1a**, suggest one problem with using BMI as a way of estimating body fat.

_____

_____

Other simple measurements of body fat include **waist : hip ratio**.

4. a. Describe how waist : hip ratio is calculated.

_____

_____

b. Describe how waist : hip ratio will change if a person's mass of fat increases.

_____

_____

c. Suggest why waist circumference or waist : hip ratio may show better correlation than BMI with the risk of developing type 2 diabetes.

_____

_____

_____

1. Two different types of **white blood cell** are **phagocytes** and **lymphocytes**. Describe how each type of cell helps to destroy foreign cells in the body.

_____

_____

2. Give **one** reason for each of the following adaptations of **erythrocytes**.

a. They are shaped like biconcave discs, with a hollow on each side.

_____

b. Unlike most cells, they do not have a nucleus.

_____

c. They are very small and flexible.

_____

3. In a sample of 1 mm³ of **blood**, there were about 4 900 000 erythrocytes, 5000 white blood cells and 250 000 **platelets**.

H a. Write the number of erythrocytes per mm³ of blood in standard form.

_____

H b. Write the number of white blood cells per mm³ of blood in standard form.

_____

c. Two quantities differ by one order of magnitude if one is 10 times bigger than the other. By approximately how many orders of magnitude do the numbers of **red blood cells** and white blood cells differ?

_____

d. 70% of white blood cells are phagocytes. How many cells is this per mm³ of blood?

_____

4. In body tissues, blood flows through a network of fine **capillaries** (a capillary bed).

artery   vein

capillary bed

a. In which direction is blood flowing in the diagram above?

_____

b. What happens to the surface area : volume (SA : V) ratio of blood vessels moving from an artery to a capillary bed?

_____

c. State why this change in SA : V ratio is useful.

_____

d. What other adaptation do capillaries have to ensure efficient exchange of substances?

_____

_____

Ash trees are the third most common species of tree in Britain. They can live to 400 years or more and are an important species in many woodland **ecosystems**. In some woodlands the ash **population** can include around half the trees. Ash trees contribute significantly to the woodland **community**.

1. State what is meant by the terms:

a. woodland ecosystem

_____

_____

b. ash population

_____

_____

c. woodland community.

_____

_____

2. Ash tree leaves are food for the caterpillars of many moth species, including the privet hawk moth. Many bird species, including bullfinches, eat ash seeds. Beetles hide in cracks in the bark of the ash trees and feed on algae or smaller insects. In fact, over 1000 species depend on ash trees for **resources**, including some species that are rare.

Describe **two** examples of different resources that ash trees provide to the woodland community.

_____

_____

_____

_____

3. The leaves on ash trees open in late spring. This means that plenty of light reaches the woodland floor in early spring. This encourages the growth of many woodland floor plants, such as dog violet.

Students carry out a survey of woodland to estimate the **abundance** of dog violets. They use **quadrats** that are 1 m². The table shows their results.

Quadrat sample	1	2	3	4	5	6	7	8	9	10	11	12	13	14	15	16	17	18	19	20
Number of violets	0	2	1	5	0	1	0	3	2	0	0	1	4	2	1	0	3	0	0	2

a. Describe how the survey should have been carried out to get an abundance value that is reasonably accurate. Give a reason for your suggested method.

_____

_____

_____

b. The total area of the woodland is 25 ha (1 ha = 10 000 m²). Use the formula below to calculate an estimate for the dog violet population size in the woodland. Show your working.

$$\text{estimated population size} = \text{total number of organisms in } \textbf{samples} \times \frac{\text{total area of study area}}{\text{total area of quadrats}}.$$

_____

You do not have to remember any details of the diagram shown on this page for your exam, but you could be asked to apply your knowledge to unfamiliar situations.

A transect is set out from the middle of an open meadow (0 m) into a wood, over a distance of 20 m. The abundance of three plant species is recorded at particular points along the transect. The results are used to produce the diagram below. The table shows the measurements made of other factors along the transect.

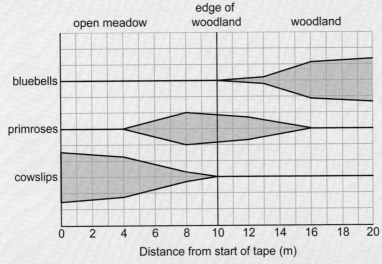

This sort of diagram is used to show the percentage cover of each plant in a sample. A horizontal line means 0 per cent (i.e. not present). The height of a 'kite shape' increases as percentage cover increases.

	Open meadow			Inside woodland		
Distance from tape end (m)	0	4	8	12	16	20
Light intensity (lux)	6430	5673	2554	833	672	587
Soil moisture (%)	28	24	27	31	34	27
Temperature (°C)	14.5	14.0	14.5	13.5	13.0	13.0

1. Describe a method for this investigation, identifying suitable measuring apparatus for each factor measured.

_____

_____

_____

2. The diagram above shows the **distribution** and abundance of some species. State the meaning of:

a. distribution_____

b. abundance_____

3. Use the diagram to identify which species is most abundant at the point 8 m from the start of the tape.

_____

4. Use the diagram to describe the change in abundance along the transect for each species.

_____

_____

_____

_____

_____

The *Toxoplasma* protist can cause the disease toxoplasmosis in humans. Up to a third of people in the UK may be infected with the protist during their lives. Most people have no symptoms, but infection can cause problems for pregnant women and harm the developing fetus. Infection can also damage the eyes, heart, lungs or brain of people whose immune systems cannot fight back. The protist infects most mammal species, including cats, pigs, mice and sheep.

1. *Toxoplasma* protists live in a close relationship with mammals.

a. State the name given to this type of relationship. _____

b. Explain your answer to part **a**.

_____

_____

Infection is usually through the mouth. Protists pass into the blood through the intestine wall. They then enter cells, usually in the muscles or brain, where they form cysts. Cysts have a coat that can protect the protist for the life of the **host**. The protist reproduces sexually only in cats, producing cysts that are shed in faeces.

2. a. Describe **two** sources of toxoplasmosis infection for humans.

_____

_____

b. Describe how the spread of infection could be reduced for people at risk of being harmed by toxoplasmosis.

_____

_____

_____

The human gut is home to many other organisms, mainly bacteria. The bacteria get the nutrients they need for growth and reproduction by digesting some of the food in the human gut. Evidence from the use of antibiotics shows that some of these bacteria are important for human health. Some of the digestion products of the bacteria come from substances that we cannot digest. Some bacteria also produce new substances, including vitamin K and folate, which we cannot synthesise but which our cells need. We absorb these useful substances.

3. The bacteria in the human gut live in a close relationship with humans.

a. State the name of the type of relationship between humans and bacteria that produce useful substances (such as vitamin K).

_____

b. Explain your answer to part **a**.

_____

_____

4. Explain how using antibiotics has provided evidence for the importance of some gut bacteria to human health.

_____

_____

_____

_____

1. The diagram shows the average annual rainfall across a section of the UK. The section runs from Manchester in the west, through a range of hills called the Pennines, east to Lincoln. Most winds blow across the UK from the west.

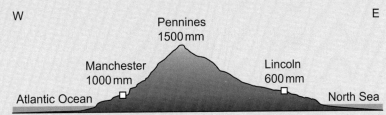

W

Pennines
1500 mm

Manchester
1000 mm

Lincoln
600 mm

Atlantic Ocean

North Sea

E

a. Use your knowledge of the **water cycle** to describe how the water content of the air changes as it crosses the Atlantic Ocean towards the UK.

_____

_____

_____

b. As clouds from the west move across the UK, they have to rise over the Pennines. Explain how this will affect the size of the clouds.

_____

_____

_____

c. Use your answer to part **b** to explain the difference in rainfall between Manchester and the Pennines.

_____

_____

_____

d. Explain the difference in rainfall between Manchester and Lincoln.

_____

_____

2. London is on the east side of the UK, and has a large human population. In 2010 the Thames Water Desalination Plant was opened. This produces enough water each day to supply about 900 000 people during times of drought.

a. Suggest **two** reasons why London is at particular risk of drought.

_____

_____

_____

b. The water used in the **desalination** plant is brackish (a mix of river and sea water). Explain why it must go through desalination to make it **potable**.

_____

_____

_____

_____

Farmers add **manure** (from animal waste) or chemical fertilisers (soluble **nitrates** and other nutrients) to fields.

1. One study compared the effects of chemical fertiliser and manure on the growth of maize. This had the following results:

- test plots in field A: no fertiliser – seed yield 3.46 tonnes per hectare (t/ha), organic fertiliser (manure spread at 5 t/ha) – seed yield 4.05 t/ha
- test plots in field B: no fertiliser – seed yield 3.68 t/ha, chemical fertiliser (spread at 400 kg/ha) – seed yield 3.83 t/ha

Explain these results.

_____

_____

_____

_____

Using chemical fertilisers or manure has both benefits and disadvantages, as shown in the table below.

	Chemical fertilisers	**Manure**
advantages	<ul><li>nutrients available immediately</li><li>deliver specific amounts of nutrient to crop</li><li>can be applied at the best time for the crop and weather conditions</li><li>no risk of pathogens</li></ul>	<ul><li>slow release of nutrients can support plant growth for longer</li><li>improves soil structure (allows more oxygen into soil, better drainage)</li><li>risk of environmental eutrophication usually lower than with fertiliser</li></ul>
disadvantages	<ul><li>contain only a few types of nutrient</li><li>do not increase soil bacteria content</li><li>expensive to produce</li><li>increased risk of eutrophication of environment</li></ul>	<ul><li>must be spread before crop planting, cannot be added afterwards</li><li>less concentrated source of nutrients than in chemical fertilisers</li><li>nutrient release depends on soil bacteria content, temperature, soil water content</li><li>may contain pathogens, weed seeds, etc.</li></ul>

2. Explain why the release of nutrients that plants need for healthy growth is slower from manure than from chemical fertilisers.

_____

_____

_____

3. Explain why the risk of environmental eutrophication is usually lower for manure than for fertiliser.

_____

_____

4. Explain why it is difficult to produce similar results in terms of crop yield year on year when using manure compared with adding chemical fertiliser.

_____

_____

_____

CB1 Key Concepts in Biology

CB1a **Microscopes**

Complete the table to compare the features of a light microscope with an electron microscope.

Feature	Light microscope	Electron microscope
Imaging using		
Maximum magnification		
Finest resolution		
Focused using		
Organisms		
Preparation of specimen		
Cost		

CB1b **Plant and animal cells**

Ribosomes were not identified until the 1950s, 300 years after Hooke and van Leeuwenhoek identified living cells. Explain why this was and what developments had taken place in that period to make this possible.

_____

_____

_____

_____

CB1d **Inside bacteria**

Some bacteria have structures called pili on their outer surfaces. These structures can allow two bacteria to join together in a process called conjugation. During this process some of the cell contents can be exchanged between the two bacteria. Explain how conjugation might change some of the activities that occur inside a bacterial cell.

_____

_____

_____

_____

CB1h **Transporting substances**

1. Explain the importance of plant cell walls in relation to **osmosis**.

_____

_____

_____

_____

2. The mass of a slice of potato is measured as 28 g. The slice is then placed into a beaker of distilled water. After 20 minutes, the slice is taken out of the water and blotted dry with a paper towel. Its new mass is 35 g.

a. Which transport process has caused the potato slice to increase in mass: diffusion, osmosis or active transport?

b. Explain as fully as you can why the potato slice increased in mass.

c. Calculate the percentage gain in mass of the potato slice, using the formula:

$$\frac{\text{final mass} - \text{initial mass}}{\text{initial mass}} \times 100\%$$

(Note: if the calculated value is positive, this shows percentage gain.)

CB2 Cells and Control

CB2a **Mitosis**

Mitotic inhibitors are substances that are found naturally in plants. These substances stop the formation of **spindle fibres**. Mitotic inhibitors can be used to treat some cancers.

a. Explain why mitotic inhibitors can be used to treat cancers.

b. Suggest **one** problem that might be caused by mitotic inhibitors.

c. It is possible to watch some cells dividing, using certain types of microscope. Suggest what you might see through this type of microscope if you looked at **cancer cells** that had just been treated with a mitotic inhibitor.

CB2c **Growth in plants**

Calculate the percentage gain in mass of **stem** and of **leaf** between 30 and 100 days at the high carbon dioxide concentration. Use your calculation to identify which part of the plant grew fastest when carbon dioxide concentrations were increased.

Carbon dioxide concentration	Dry mass at 30 days (mg)		Dry mass at 100 days (mg)	
	stem	leaf	stem	leaf
normal atmospheric	0.001	0.009	0.069	0.595
high	0.002	0.015	0.069	0.656

CB2f **Neurotransmission speeds**

If a bacterium called *Clostridium tetani* gets into humans it can produce a poison that causes a serious condition called tetanus. The poison blocks the release of glycine into synapses. What do you think the symptoms of tetanus are? Explain your reasoning.

_____

_____

_____

_____

CB3 Genetics

CB3a **Meiosis**

The diagram shows the nuclei of two gamete-making cells, both from the same organism.

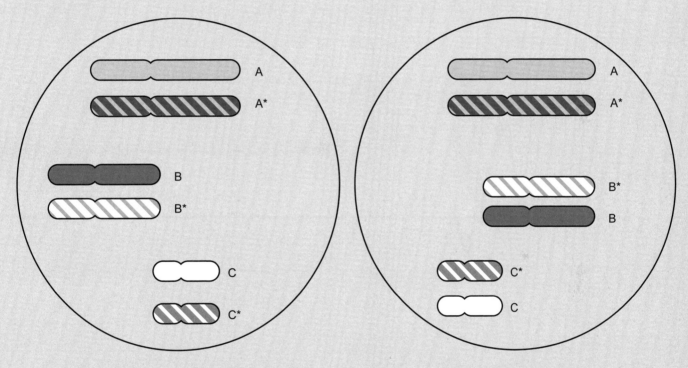

Extend the diagram to explain how an organism makes haploid gametes that are genetically different from one another. You do not have to draw the chromosomes exactly as they are drawn above.

CB3c **Alleles**

The phenotype for pea plant A is yellow pods and green pea coats. This plant has yellow pods because of a recessive allele for pod colour. The coat around its peas is green because the plant is heterozygous for the allele that causes pea coat colour.

Pea plant B is homozygous for the dominant allele for pod colour, and so has green pods. It is homozygous for the recessive allele for pea coat colour, and so its peas have white coats.

Plants A and B are crossed. Predict the ratio of phenotypes for the offspring.

CB3e **Gene mutation**

In 2012, scientists announced that they had developed a GM tomato that produced a protein that would lower cholesterol in the blood and reduce the build-up of fatty deposits (plaques) in the blood vessels. Do you think that gardeners should be able to buy seeds for these tomatoes and grow them at home? Explain your reasoning.

_____

_____

_____

_____

_____

_____

_____

_____

_____

_____

_____

_____

_____

CB4 Natural Selection and Genetic Modification

CB4c **Classification**

Find out how the cell walls of Archaea are different from those of bacteria.

_____

_____

CB4e Genes in agriculture and medicine

Resistance to insecticide in mosquitoes occurs as a result of changes in genes (mutations). These changes then stop the insecticide harming the mosquito. Explain how widespread use of an insecticide could rapidly lead to the mosquito population becoming resistant to the insecticide.

_____

_____

_____

_____

_____

_____

CB5 Health, Disease and the Development of Medicines

CB5f Physical and chemical barriers

In 2013, the national _Chlamydia_ screening programme for 15–24-year-olds carried out 531 428 tests on males and 1 177 005 tests on females. The total number of males in this age group was estimated at 3 519 015 and the total number of females was estimated at 3 388 842.

a. Calculate the percentage of males and of females that were tested in 2013.

_____

b. A simple conclusion from the graph on page 18 is that a greater percentage of 15- to 24-year-old females are infected than 15- to 24-year-old males. Use your calculations in **a** to judge how valid that conclusion is.

_____

_____

_____

_____

CB5h Antibiotics

Question **5** on page 19 describes research carried out on the new antibiotic teixobactin.

There are millions of species of soil bacteria. Suggest an explanation for why _Eleftheria terrae_ makes teixobactin.

_____

_____

_____

CB6 Plant Structures and their Functions

CB6b Factors that affect photosynthesis

Ⓗ A bulb gives out a light intensity of 4000 lux at a distance of 5 cm. At what distance must the bulb be to produce a light intensity of 750 lux? Give your answer to the nearest half centimetre.

$$I_{new} = \frac{I_{orig} \times d^2_{orig}}{d^2_{new}}$$

CB6d Transpiration and translocation

A student carries out an experiment using the **potometer** shown and an electric fan, which is set at different powers.

The results are shown in the table below.

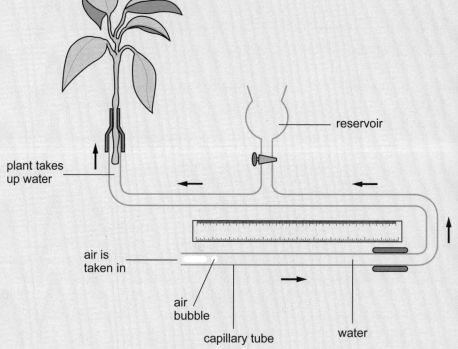

Fan power setting (W)	Distance moved by bubble in five minutes (mm)					
	Trial 1	Trial 2	Trial 3	Mean (mm)	Mean rate (mm/min)	Mean rate (mm³/min)
10	22	27	26	25	5	
15	35	36	34	35	7	
20	42	44	49	45	9	
25	55	57	56	55	11	

The volume of a cylinder is calculated using this equation: $V = \pi r^2 h$

where V is the volume

π is pi (which is equal to about 3.142, but you should use the π button on your calculator)

r is the radius and h is the height (or length).

Use the equation to calculate the rates of transpiration in units of mm³ of water per minute for each fan setting. The diameter of the potometer tube is 1.3 mm.

CB7 Animal Coordination, Control and Homeostasis
CB7a **Hormones**

Describe how neurotransmitters are different from hormones.

_____

_____

_____

_____

CB7d **Hormones and the menstrual cycle**

H IVF treatment costs thousands of pounds for each attempt. The chart shows results from a US study in 2013 on the effect of the mother's age and number of IVF attempts on the chance of a live birth.

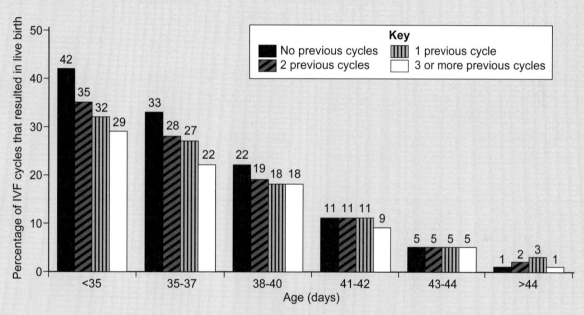

Use the information above and in the graph to explain the following recommendations in the UK.

a. Only one IVF treatment is free.

_____

_____

b. Treatment is usually offered only to women under the age of 35 years.

_____

_____

_____

c. The maximum number of IVF cycles is three.

_____

_____

_____

_____

CB8 Exchange and Transport in Animals

CB8b The circulatory system

People can faint when their brains do not get enough oxygen. Soldiers who have to stand still for long periods of time often faint. Explain this observation.

_____

_____

_____

_____

CB9 Ecosystems and Material Cycles

CB9a Ecosystems

Ash trees are the third most common species of tree in Britain. They can live to 400 years or more and are an important species in many woodland **ecosystems**. In some woodlands the ash **population** can include around half the trees. Ash trees contribute significantly to the woodland **community**.

Chalara dieback is a disease of ash trees that was first seen in the UK in 2012. The disease kills ash trees over several years, although there is evidence that young trees are more rapidly affected than older trees. Many people are concerned about the possible impact of chalara dieback on British woodlands.

Not all ash trees in a woodland are affected by chalara dieback. Scientists are studying the genetics of trees that are affected and those that are not.

a. Give a reason why genetics might explain the difference in how trees are affected by the disease.

_____

_____

b. Explain how any genetic difference could be used to help restore damaged woodlands.

_____

_____

_____

_____

CB9b Abiotic factors and communities

A student observes that bluebells in a bright part of the wood wilt during the hottest part of a still day (no wind). He suggests that air humidity (the amount of water in the air) might account for the bluebell distribution along the transect. Use your knowledge of transpiration to explain this suggestion.

_____

_____

_____

_____

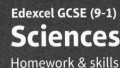

Sciences   CC1a States of matter
Homework & skills

1. a. Name the three **states of matter**.

_____

b. Name the **physical changes** that occur between states of matter, and specify which states are involved in each change.

_____

_____

_____

c. Name the state of a substance in which the mean energy of its **particles** is generally lowest.

_____

2. Describe the arrangements and movement of particles of:

a. water in a swimming pool _____

b. water in an ice cube _____

c. the air around you _____

3. Explain, in terms of **attractive forces** between particles, why:

a. energy must be transferred from the surroundings to the particles during boiling

_____

_____

b. energy is transferred to the surroundings from the particles during freezing.

_____

_____

4. The table shows some **melting points** and **boiling points**.

Substance	Melting point (°C)	Boiling point (°C)
ethanol	−114	78
ammonia	−78	−33
fluorine	−220	−188
mercury	−39	357

a. Complete the table to show the state of each substance at the temperature shown.

Temperature (°C)	ethanol	ammonia	fluorine	mercury
215				
0				
−215				

b. Ethanol and mercury are both used in making thermometers. Scientists use 'ultra-low' freezers to store heat-sensitive substances at −40 °C to −85 °C. Explain which type of thermometer, ethanol or mercury, would be most suitable for use in these freezers.

_____

_____

_____

_____

1. Write definitions for the following key words:

a. physical property

_____

_____

b. mixture

_____

_____

c. pure

_____

_____

d. impure

_____

_____

e. heating curve

_____

_____

f. melting point

_____

_____

2. Explain how you can use melting point data to identify whether a substance is pure or a mixture.

_____

_____

_____

_____

3. Explain, in no more than 50 words, why pure substances have fixed melting points, but mixtures do not.

_____

_____

_____

_____

A forger altered a cheque by changing the amount from 'seven' to 'seventy'. A forensic scientist was asked to find out who had done it.

The cheque was cut up and the black ink from the 'ty' of the 'seventy' and the '0' of the '70' were dissolved in ethanol. There were four suspects – A, B, C and D.

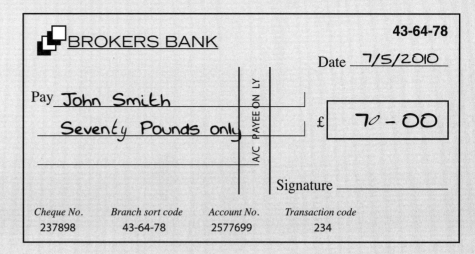

BROKERS BANK   43-64-78

Date 7/5/2010

Pay John Smith

Seventy Pounds only   £ 70 - 00

A/C PAYEE ONLY

Signature _____

Cheque No.   Branch sort code   Account No.   Transaction code
237898   43-64-78   2577699   234

They were each asked for the black pen they use. A **chromatogram** was produced from the ink on the cheque, and the inks from the pens of the four suspects.

1. Describe the steps that the forensic scientist would have to carry out to make the chromatogram shown.

_____

_____

_____

_____

_____

_____

_____

_____

_____

_____

_____

_____

_____

_____

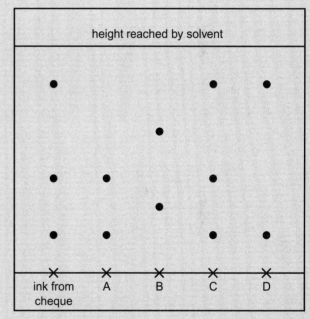

height reached by solvent

ink from   A   B   C   D
cheque

2. How many dyes were in the ink from the cheque? _____

3. a. Which suspect's pen was definitely **not** used to forge the cheque? _____

b. Explain your answer to part **a.**

_____

_____

4. Calculate the **R$_f$ value** for each dye in the ink from the cheque.

_____

1. a. Name **three** different natural sources of fresh water.

_____

b. Explain why water obtained from the sources named in part **a** must be treated before drinking it.

_____

_____

c. Describe the main steps, and the reason for each step, involved in treating fresh water to produce drinking water.

_____

_____

_____

_____

2. Silver nitrate solution is used to detect chloride salts dissolved in water. The solution reacts with the salts to produce a cloudy, white precipitate of silver chloride. Seawater contains about 27 g/dm^3 sodium chloride and tap water contains about 0.41 g/dm^3.

a. Explain what you would expect to observe when a few drops of silver nitrate solution are added to a sample of seawater.

_____

b. A school technician dissolves some silver nitrate in tap water. Explain what the technician would observe.

_____

_____

c. Explain why the technician would not use tap water for **chemical analysis**.

_____

3. Ethanol is a colourless liquid that mixes completely with water and boils at 78 °C. Table salt and table sugar are white solids. They are both soluble in water, but only sugar is soluble in ethanol.

Describe and explain:

a. what you would expect to see if you added a mixture of salt and sugar to water, and to ethanol

_____

_____

b. how you could obtain dry salt from a mixture of salt and sugar

_____

_____

c. how you could separate ethanol from a mixture of ethanol and water.

_____

_____

_____

_____

With the discovery of new evidence, most scientific theories change and develop over the years. Atomic structure is a good example of a theory that has changed over the last 200 years as new evidence has been obtained.

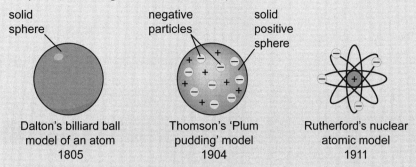

| Dalton's billiard ball model of an atom 1805 | Thomson's 'Plum pudding' model 1904 | Rutherford's nuclear atomic model 1911 |

The first model represents John Dalton's 'tiny solid particles' that make up all matter. Then, almost 100 years later, after the discovery of charged particles, JJ Thomson proposed his 'plum-pudding' model. At the start of the twentieth century there was increased interest in investigating theories about **atoms**. This led to further evidence of charged particles and how they were arranged inside the atom. This resulted in Ernest Rutherford's model with each atom having a small positive central mass.

1. How did Dalton's ideas about atoms help to explain the difference between **elements**?

_____

_____

2. Look at Thomson's 'plum-pudding' model.

a. Suggest a name for the negatively charged particles in this model. _____

b. Why do you think it was called the 'plum-pudding' model?

_____

_____

3. How could Thomson's atomic model be used to explain the differences between elements?

_____

_____

_____

4. a. Draw a diagram of the modern model of an atom, labelling the **nucleus** and the **electrons**.

b. What feature was introduced in the modern atomic model that wasn't in Dalton's or Thomson's models?

_____

c. What feature of the structure of an atom is not shown well by your drawing?

_____

_____

Sciences CC3b Atomic number and mass number

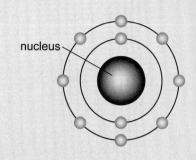

1. Write a description of the atomic model shown in this diagram. Your description should include an explanation of:

- where the protons and neutrons are found
- how the electrons are arranged
- the charges on the different subatomic particles
- where the mass of the atom is concentrated
- how the model could be improved so that it would describe our ideas about atoms better.

_____

_____

_____

_____

_____

_____

_____

_____

_____

_____

2. Use this table to answer the questions below.

Atom	Atomic number	Mass number	Number of ...		
			protons	electrons	neutrons
A	5	11	5	5	6
B	10	20	10	10	10
C	48	110	48	48	62
D	10	22	10	10	12

a. Which atom has the greatest mass? Explain your answer.

_____

_____

b. Which **two** atoms are of the same element? Explain your answer.

_____

_____

c. Which atom has twice the mass of atom **A**? Explain your answer.

_____

_____

d. If you had 10 g of atom **D**, what mass of atom **C** would contain the same number of atoms? Explain your answer.

_____

_____

_____

Sciences
CC3c Isotopes
Homework & skills

Chemical reactions cannot change one element into another because they don't affect the nuclei of atoms. However, we can form new elements using the **nuclear fission** reaction in nuclear power stations. Nuclear fission occurs when large atoms such as uranium-235 are bombarded with neutrons and split apart to make smaller, new atoms. New elements with smaller nuclei are formed. Energy is also transferred, which can be used to produce electricity.

1. Explain why chemical reactions cannot be used to make different elements.

_____

_____

_____

2. Neutron bombardment of uranium-235 can result in nuclear fission and the production of new elements as shown.

Complete the table below with information about the atoms of the elements involved in this nuclear fission reaction.

This is just one example of the fission products that can be produced.

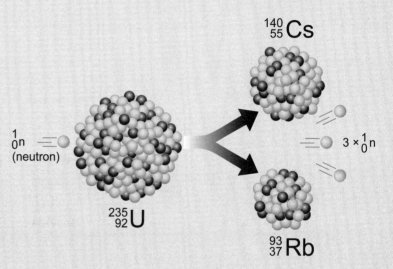

$^{140}_{55}\text{Cs}$

$^{1}_{0}\text{n}$
(neutron)

$3 \times ^{1}_{0}\text{n}$

$^{235}_{92}\text{U}$

$^{93}_{37}\text{Rb}$

Element	Notation in the form $^{A}_{Z}X$	Atomic number	Mass number	Number of		
				protons	neutrons	electrons
uranium, U						
caesium, Cs						
rubidium, Rb						

3. Nuclear fission changes can be shown using nuclear equations. The large atom and the bombarding neutrons at the start are shown on the left, and the new atoms produced are shown on the right.

The nuclear equation below shows the fission that occurs in question **3**. How many protons and neutrons are on each side of this nuclear equation?

$$^{235}_{92}\text{U} + ^{1}_{0}\text{n} \rightarrow ^{140}_{55}\text{Cs} + ^{93}_{37}\text{Rb} + 3\,^{1}_{0}\text{n}$$

_____

4. The element boron has two **isotopes**, $^{11}_{5}\text{B}$ and $^{10}_{5}\text{B}$, in the ratio 4:1.

a. In terms of subatomic particles, what is the difference between these two atoms?

_____

⊞ b. Use the information to calculate the **relative atomic mass** of boron.

_____

1. Part of Dmitri Mendeleev's 1871 table is shown below. Use it to help you answer the questions. (Refer to the periodic table on the back inside cover if you need to.)

Li 7	Be 9.4	B 11	C 12	N 14	O 16	F 19
Na 23	Mg 24	Al 27.3	Si 28	P 31	S 32	Cl 35.5
K 39	Ca 40	? 44	Ti 48	V 51	Cr 52	Mn 55

a. Name each element in the middle row.

_____

b. What property did Mendeleev use to order the elements in his tables?

_____

c. How are the elements arranged in the rows of Mendeleev's 1871 table?

_____

d. What do the elements in each column have in common?

_____

e. Explain why Mendeleev showed an element with a question mark in the bottom row.

_____

2. The existence of eka-silicon, Es, was predicted by Mendeleev in 1871. He thought it should fit between silicon and tin. Germanium, Ge, was discovered in 1886 by Clemens Winkler. It was identified as Mendeleev's predicted element. Some properties of these elements and their compounds are shown below.

Element	Relative atomic mass	Density (g/cm³)	Density of its chloride (g/cm³)	Boiling point of its chloride (°C)
silicon	28	2.3	1.48	58
eka-silicon	72	5.5	1.9	100
germanium	73	5.3	1.88	86
tin	118	7.4	2.22	114

a. Calculate a mean value for each property using the values for silicon and tin.

_____

b. Compare your answers to part **a** with Mendeleev's **predictions**. How close are they?

_____

_____

c. Describe how close Mendeleev's predictions for eka-silicon were to the actual properties of germanium.

_____

_____

_____

d. When germanium was first discovered, Winkler thought it was eka-stibnium, a different predicted element. Mendeleev thought it could be yet another predicted element, eka-cadmium. After Winkler purified more of the new element, he was able to provide more accurate values for its properties and its identity was confirmed. Describe the importance of accurate values in supporting Mendeleev's table.

_____

_____

Use this short form periodic table to help you answer the questions. It shows symbols and atomic numbers.

group numbers

	1	2	3	4	5	6	7	0
1	H 1							He 2
2	Li 3	Be 4	B 5	C 6	N 7	O 8	F 9	Ne 10
3	Na 11	Mg 12	Al 13	Si 14	P 15	S 16	Cl 17	Ar 18
4	K 19	Ca 20						

period numbers

1. State what is meant by the term '**electronic configuration**'.

_____

_____

2. Write the electronic configurations for helium, carbon, oxygen, chlorine and calcium.

_____

_____

_____

3. Draw the electronic configurations for nitrogen and argon.

4. The electronic configuration of an element is related to its position in the periodic table.

a. Explain how the group in which an element is placed is related to its electronic configuration. In your answer, refer to the elements in groups 1 and 0.

_____

_____

_____

b. Explain how the period in which an element is placed is related to its electronic configuration. In your answer, refer to the elements in period 2.

_____

_____

_____

Sciences **CC5a** Ionic bonds
Homework & skills

1. Describe how **cations** and **anions** form in terms of electron transfer.

Because they are adoped for there fulran

2. Complete the table below. One row has been done for you.

Element	Electron arrangement	Group number	Metal or non-metal	Electrons lost or gained	How many electrons	Charge on ion	Ion symbol
Li	2.1	1	metal	lost	1	1+	Li⁺
Na	2.2		non mad		2	2+	Na t
Mg	2.3		metal		3	1+	mg ⁻
Al	2.4		metal		4	4+	al ⁺
O	2.5		~~metal~~ Non metal		5	1+	O⁻
S	1.5		metal		6	1+	S+
F	1.7		metal		7	1+	F⁻
Cl	1.8		metal		8	1+	Cl⁺

3. Look at your completed table for question **2**.

a. State the link between an element's group number and the size of the charge formed on its positive or negative **ion**.

they are Smaller in Sice

b. What is the difference between metals and non-metals in terms of the type of ion formed?

Sone are non - meleels

4. Information about ions can be written using the notation shown below.

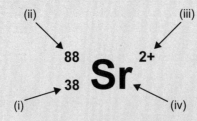

(ii)   (iii)

$$^{88}_{38}Sr^{2+}$$

(i)   (iv)

a. What information about the ion is shown at **(i)** to **(iv)** in the diagram above?

i   mays number   ii   prous an puham

iii   atcue number   iv   Sybol

b. How many protons, neutrons and electrons are in the ion?

48

Kilns are hot ovens with many uses, for example, drying wood and making ceramics from clay. For some uses, the temperature inside the kiln can reach over 1000 °C. It is important that the inside of the kiln does not melt. Aluminium oxide is used to coat the inside of some kilns. Aluminium oxide is an ionic compound with a melting point of 2054 °C.

Silver is an expensive metal. Instead of making objects such as jewellery and trophies out of solid silver, they can be made of another less expensive metal and then coated with a layer of silver. This is called silver plating. The object being plated with silver is placed into an electrical circuit as the negative electrode in a solution of an ionic compound of silver, such as silver nitrate, along with a piece of silver as the positive electrode. The solution of silver nitrate conducts electricity and the metal object is coated with silver.

1. Give the formulae of:

a. aluminium oxide (ions present: Al^{3+} and O^{2-}) _____

b. silver nitrate (ions present: Ag^+ and NO_3^-). _____

2. Explain why aluminium oxide has a high melting point.

_____

_____

_____

3. Sodium chloride is an ionic compound with a melting point of 801 °C. Explain why:

a. sodium chloride would not be suitable to coat the inside of kilns

_____

_____

b. sodium chloride has a much lower melting point than aluminium oxide.

_____

_____

_____

_____

_____

4. Silver nitrate solution is used in electroplating because it conducts electricity. Explain why silver nitrate solution conducts electricity.

_____

_____

_____

5. Explain why solid aluminium oxide and solid silver nitrate do not conduct electricity.

_____

_____

Sciences **CC6a** Covalent bonds
Homework & skills

1. Our atmosphere is a mixture of **elements** and **compounds**, which are mainly made up of single **atoms** or small **molecules**. In the molecules, the atoms are held together by **covalent bonds**.

a. Write a sentence to explain or describe each of the terms in bold in the above passage.

_____

_____

_____

_____

_____

_____

_____

b. Name and give the formula of each of the substances in our atmosphere shown below.

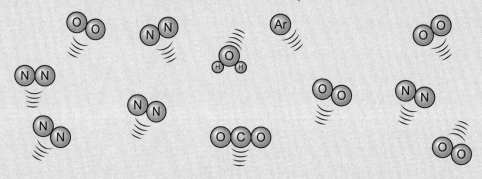

_____

c. Choose **one** chemical in our atmosphere that fits each of the descriptions below.

    i   an element _____

    ii a compound _____

    iii made up of molecules _____

    iv made up of single atoms _____

2. The diagram below shows some molecules of carbon dioxide.

a. Label the 'strong covalent bonds' and 'weak forces of attraction'.

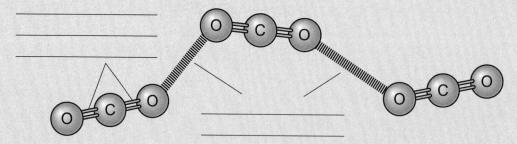

b. These forces and bonds are described as 'electrostatic'. What are **electrostatic forces** of attraction?

_____

_____

c. Why are there two lines between the carbon and oxygen atoms in the molecules?

_____

_____

The graph below shows the melting and boiling points of molecules containing different numbers of carbon atoms.

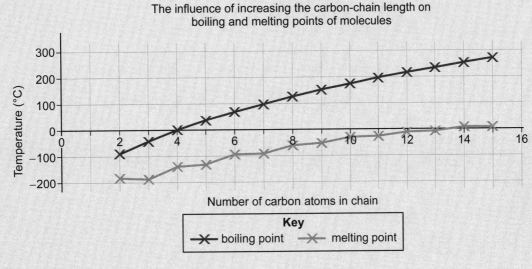

The influence of increasing the carbon-chain length on boiling and melting points of molecules

Key
boiling point   melting point

1. Look at the graph.

a. Describe the pattern seen for the melting and boiling points.

_____

_____

_____

b. Explain these patterns using your knowledge of structure, bonding and forces.

_____

_____

_____

2. Would you expect any of these molecules to conduct electricity? Explain your answer.

_____

_____

3. Neither ethene nor **poly(ethene)** is represented on the graph above. Ethene contains just two carbon atoms and is the name of the **monomer** that reacts to form the long-chain **polymer**, poly(ethene). Poly(ethene) has a melting range of between 115 and 135 °C. Use your knowledge of the properties of polymers to answer the questions.

a. Estimate the temperature at which you would expect ethene to melt. _____

b. What effect does joining monomers to form the polymer poly(ethene) have on the melting temperature?

_____

c. A molecule containing 60 carbon atoms melts at 100 °C. What might be deduced from the fact that the melting temperature of poly(ethene) is greater than 100 °C?

_____

d. Explain why poly(ethene) has a range of melting temperatures and not a fixed melting point.

_____

_____

CC7c Properties of metals

1. State **two** characteristic properties of:

a. metals ______________________________

b. non-metals ______________________________

2. The diagram below shows one way in which the ions in a metal can be arranged.

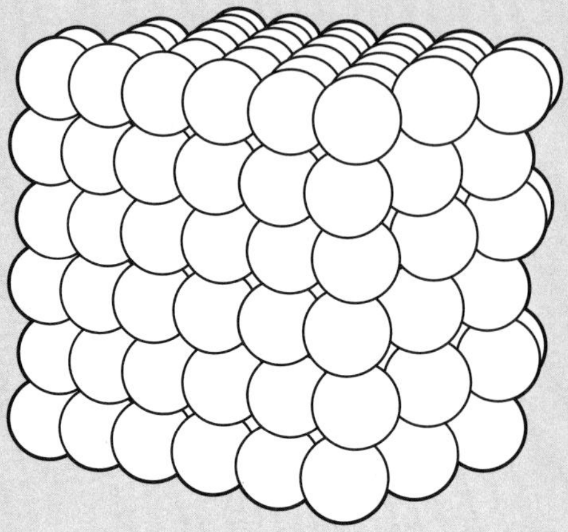

Explain how the particles are held together in a metal.

____

____

3. Explain why metals are **malleable**.

____

____

4. Explain why metals conduct electricity.

____

____

5. The diagram below shows a small section of the structure of diamond.

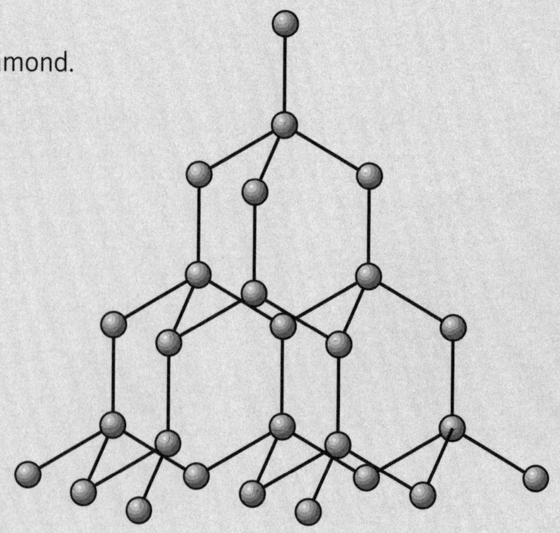

a. State **one** similarity and **two** differences in the properties of a piece of copper and a diamond.

____

____

b. Describe how the bonding in copper and diamond accounts for the differences in their properties.

____

____

____

____

____

____

1. The pH scale is used to measure how **acidic** or **alkaline** a solution is. The table below shows the pH of six solutions.

Solution	A	B	C	D	E	F
pH	1	3	6	7	9	10

a. Describe how you could test the pH of a solution.

_____

_____

b. Which of the solutions in the table are acidic? _____

c. Which of the solutions contain excess OH⁻ ions? _____

H d. Which of the solutions contains the highest concentration of H⁺ ions? _____

e. State what would happen to the pH if pure water were added to:

    i   solution D _____

    ii solution E _____

H 2. Look at the diagrams below that model the concentration of ions in different solutions.

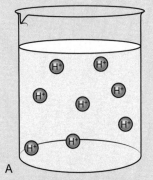
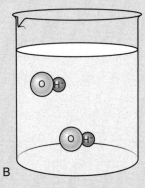
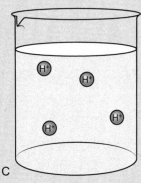
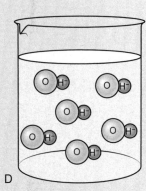

A   B   C   D

a. List the beakers in order of increasing pH value _____

b. Explain how you worked out the order in your answer to part **a**.

_____

_____

3. The table below gives the colour of universal indictor at different pH values.

pH of solution	1	2	3	4	5	6	7	8	9	10	11	12	13	14
Universal indicator colour	red	red	red	red/orange	orange	yellow	green	green/blue	blue	blue/purple	purple	purple	purple	purple

a. What colour change in universal indicator occurs when:

    H i   water is added to an acid with a pH of 1 _____

       ii alkali is added to a neutral solution _____

b. If a solution turns universal indicator purple, what colour would the following indicators have in the same solution?

    i   litmus   ii phenolphthalein   iii methyl orange

    _____   _____   _____

Sciences   CC8c Bases and salts
Homework & skills

1. Use the substances in the box below to answer the questions that follow.

magnesium chloride	sulfuric acid	water	zinc oxide	iron nitrate
cobalt oxide	nitric acid	copper oxide	cobalt sulfate	hydrochloric acid

a. Which of these substances are bases?

_____

b. Which of these substances are salts?

_____

c. Which **two** substances could be used to make zinc nitrate?

_____

d. Write a word equation for a neutralisation reaction using only substances named in the box.

_____

2. Complete the following equations, including adding state symbols. All the salts dissolve in water.

a. _____ + _____ → $MgSO_4$ + H_2O

b. H_2SO_4 + NiO → _____ + _____

c. _____ + _____ → $CoSO_4$ + H_2O

3. Use the ion charges in the box to write formulae for the following substances:

Li^+	Mg^{2+}	Al^{3+}	Cl^-	$(SO_4)^{2-}$	$(NO_3)^-$

a. lithium chloride	**b.** magnesium chloride	**c.** aluminium chloride
_____	_____	_____
d. lithium sulfate	**e.** magnesium sulfate	**f.** aluminium sulfate
_____	_____	_____
g. lithium nitrate	**h.** magnesium nitrate	**i.** aluminium nitrate
_____	_____	_____

4. Copper sulfate is made by reacting a solid black base with an acid.

a. Name the base and acid used to make copper sulfate.

_____

b. Describe the advantages of heating the acid used in this reaction.

_____

_____

c. State why an excess of the base is used.

_____

d. How can you be sure an excess of the base has been used?

_____

1. Alkalis can neutralise acids.

a. Explain, in terms of ions, what happens during neutralisation.

_____

_____

b. Describe where the ions shown in your answer to part **a** come from.

_____

_____

2. Titration must be used to prepare soluble salts from an acid and an alkali. One example of this involves the reaction of dilute sulfuric acid with sodium hydroxide solution.

a. Name the salt formed in this reaction. _____

b. Explain why titration must be used to prepare this salt using dilute sulfuric acid and sodium hydroxide solution.

_____

_____

c. Write a balanced equation for the reaction. Include state symbols in your answer.

_____

_____

3. Name the most suitable pieces of apparatus to use in a titration to:

a. measure a fixed, repeatable volume of alkali _____

b. add acid to an alkali in a conical flask _____

4. The end-point in a titration can be determined using an indicator solution.

a. Name a suitable indicator to use in a titration. _____

b. A few drops of the indicator named in part **a** are put into an acid. Describe the colour change you expect to see when an excess of alkali is added.

_____

5. a. Describe how to carry out an acid–alkali titration. Include just the essential apparatus and steps.

_____

_____

_____

_____

_____

b. Describe **two** precautions for safe working when carrying out a titration.

_____

_____

c. Describe **two** precautions to obtain an accurate titre.

_____

_____

_____

The box below shows the solubilities of some substances in water. Use this to help you answer the questions.

- All common sodium, potassium and ammonium salts are soluble.
- All nitrates are soluble.
- Most chlorides are soluble except those of silver and lead.
- Most sulfates are soluble except those of lead, barium and calcium.
- Most carbonates and hydroxides are insoluble except those of sodium, potassium and ammonium.

1. Barium nitrate is soluble.

a. Give the name of a soluble carbonate. _____

b. Write the word equation for the reaction between a solution of barium nitrate and a solution of the compound you have named in **a**. Underline the name of the precipitate formed.

_____

_____

2. Lead sulfate is insoluble.

a. Give the names of **two** solutions that will react to form a precipitate of lead sulfate.

_____

b. Describe how to obtain a pure, dry sample of lead sulfate from the solutions you have named in **a**.

_____

_____

_____

_____

_____

_____

_____

3. Copper carbonate is insoluble.

a. Give the names of **two** solutions that will react to form a precipitate of copper carbonate.

_____

b. Write the balanced equation for the reaction in **a**, including state symbols.

_____

4. Write balanced equations, including state symbols, for the precipitation reactions that happen when solutions containing the following compounds are mixed together:

a. sodium hydroxide, NaOH, and barium chloride, $BaCl_2$

_____

b. barium chloride, $BaCl_2$, and potassium sulfate, K_2SO_4

_____

c. silver nitrate, $AgNO_3$, and ammonium chloride, NH_4Cl

_____

d. ammonium carbonate, $(NH_4)_2CO_3$, and calcium nitrate, $Ca(NO_3)_2$

_____

Element	H	C	N	O	Al	S	K	Fe
Relative atomic mass (A$_r$)	1	12	14	16	27	32	39	56

1. Calculate the **relative formula mass** of each of the following compounds.

a. Al_2O_3 _____

b. $(NH_4)_2CO_3$ _____

c. $Fe(NO_3)_3$ _____

2. Write the **empirical formula** of each of the following substances.

a. C_6H_6 _____

b. C_4H_8O _____

c. $C_8H_6O_4$ _____

3. State the difference between an empirical formula and a **molecular formula**.

_____

_____

4. A compound contains 2.88 g of carbon, 0.48 g of hydrogen and 3.84 g of oxygen. The relative formula mass of the compound is 180.

Calculate:

a. the empirical formula of the compound

_____

b. the molecular formula of the compound.

_____

5. Describe an experiment that will enable you to determine the empirical formula of magnesium oxide. Include the measurements you need to take.

_____

_____

_____

_____

_____

Element	H	C	N	O	Na	Mg	S	Cl	K	Ca	Ag
Relative atomic mass (A_r)	1	12	14	16	23	24	32	35.5	39	40	108

The **Avogadro constant** is 6.02×10^{23} mol^{-1}.

 1. Calculate the number of **moles** of:

   a. oxygen molecules, O_2, in 96 g of oxygen _____

   b. oxygen atoms, O, in 96 g of oxygen. _____

 2. Calculate the mass of:

   a. 1.25 mol of potassium carbonate, K_2CO_3

   b. 0.25 mol of calcium hydroxide, $Ca(OH)_2$.

 3. Calculate the number of molecules in:

   a. 0.375 mol of carbon dioxide, CO_2

   b. 2.75 mol of oxygen, O_2.

 4. Calculate the number of moles in:

   a. 7.525×10^{22} atoms of iron

   b. 1.0535×10^{24} atoms of zinc.

 5. Calculate the number of molecules in:

   a. 42 g of nitrogen, N_2

   b. 0.48 g of oxygen, O_2.

 6. Calculate the mass of the following numbers of molecules.

   a. 6.02×10^{25} molecules of propane, C_3H_8

   b. 3.01×10^{21} molecules of water, H_2O.

Sciences **CC10a** Electrolysis
Homework & skills

1. Lead bromide does not conduct electricity when it is a solid but does conduct when it is molten.

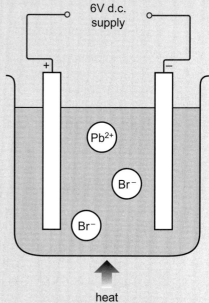

a. Give a reason why lead bromide does not conduct electricity when it is a solid.

_____

b. State which of the **electrodes** in the diagram is the **cathode**.

_____

c. State the direction in which the bromide ions move when the power is turned on.

_____

H d. Write the **half equation** for the reaction of the lead ions to form molten lead. Include state symbols.

_____

H e. Explain whether the reaction in **d** is **oxidation**, **reduction** or neither.

_____

H f. Write the half equation for the reaction of the bromide ions to form bromine gas. Include state symbols.

_____

H g. Explain whether the reaction in **f** is oxidation, reduction or neither.

_____

2. Molten sodium chloride, containing Na^+ and Cl^- ions, is electrolysed to produce molten sodium and chlorine gas.

a. Give the name of the electrode at which sodium is produced. _____

H b. Write the half equation for the formation of sodium. Include state symbols.

_____

H c. Explain whether the reaction in **b** is oxidation, reduction or neither.

_____

d. Give the name of the electrode at which chlorine is produced. _____

H e. Write the half equation for the formation of chlorine.

_____

H f. Explain whether the reaction in **e** is oxidation, reduction or neither.

_____

1. Four metals, J, K, L and M, were heated with different metal oxides. The results are shown in the table.

Metal oxide	Metal J	Metal K	Metal L	Metal M
oxide of metal J		no reaction	no reaction	no reaction
oxide of metal K	reaction		no reaction	reaction
oxide of metal L	reaction	reaction		reaction
oxide of metal M	reaction	no reaction	no reaction	

a. Place the four metals in order of reactivity, with the most reactive first.

_____

b. Give reasons for the order you have suggested.

_____

_____

_____

_____

2. Write balanced equations for the following reactions.

a. calcium with water   _____

b. zinc with hydrochloric acid   _____

3. Predict whether each of these reactions will take place. Either complete the balanced equation or write 'no reaction'.

a.   Ca +   FeO →   _____

b.   Cu +   ZnO →   _____

c.   Zn +   FeO →   _____

d.   Al +   CuO →   _____

e.   Mg + $AgNO_3$ →   _____

f.   Ag + $ZnSO_4$ →   _____

4. When calcium reacts with water, it forms a calcium ion, Ca^{2+}.

a. Explain what happens to a calcium atom when it becomes a calcium ion.

_____

b. Magnesium is lower in the **reactivity series** than calcium. Explain whether calcium atoms or magnesium atoms form **cations** more readily.

_____

_____

_____

_____

Zinc is found as zinc sulfide (ZnS) in an **ore** called zinc blende. It is obtained by one of two processes:

the **thermal process** where zinc is extracted from an ore (that contains a mixture of zinc sulfide and lead sulfide) and the **electrolytic process**. About 7.1 million tonnes of zinc is produced worldwide each year.

i *The thermal process*

Step 1   The ore is heated with air. Both metal sulfides are converted to metal oxides.

$$2ZnS + 3O_2 \rightarrow 2ZnO + 2SO_2 \qquad 2PbS + 3O_2 \rightarrow 2PbO + 2SO_2$$

Step 2   The oxides are then heated with carbon to convert them to the metals.

$$2ZnO + C \rightarrow 2Zn + CO_2 \qquad 2PbO + C \rightarrow 2Pb + CO_2$$

Step 3   The zinc is separated from the lead.

ii *The electrolytic process*

Step 1 The ore is concentrated and purified to remove lead sulfide.

Step 2 Zinc sulfide is heated in air to convert it to zinc oxide.

Step 3 The zinc oxide reacts with sulfuric acid to form zinc sulfate solution.

$$ZnO + H_2SO_4 \rightarrow ZnSO_4 + H_2O$$

Step 4 The zinc sulfate is electrolysed to form zinc. This zinc is 99.96 per cent pure.

- Price of zinc: £1.24 per kg.   Price of lead: £1.27 per kg.
- Current reserves of zinc will last 30–40 years at current rate of use and lead will last 40–50 years.
- Advantages of mining ores: it provides people with jobs and creates wealth for the local community and the country.
- Disadvantages of mining ores: the effect on the environment, the amount of waste left when the metal is removed from the ore, subsidence in underground mines, ores are non-renewable, loss of employment when the mine closes.

1. Explain the pollution problem associated with either of these methods of extracting zinc.

_____

_____

_____

2. The electrolytic process is more expensive than the thermal process but about 80 per cent of zinc is produced by the electrolytic process.

a. Suggest why the electrolytic process is more expensive than the thermal process.

_____

_____

b. Suggest why more zinc is produced using the electrolytic process than the thermal process.

_____

_____

_____

3. State an advantage, apart from cost, of the thermal process for obtaining zinc.

_____

_____

_____

_____

1. The word equation for the Haber process is shown below.

$$\text{hydrogen} \quad + \quad \text{nitrogen} \quad \rightleftharpoons \quad \text{ammonia}$$

a. Write a balanced equation for the reaction with state symbols.

_____

b. What does this sign '$\rightleftharpoons$' tell us about the reaction?

_____

c. What does the term 'dynamic' refer to in dynamic equilibrium?

_____

_____

2. If calcium carbonate is heated in a sealed test tube, an equilibrium is established.

$$CaCO_3(s) \quad \rightleftharpoons \quad CaO(s) \quad + \quad CO_2(g)$$

a. Write an equation for the forward reaction.

_____

b. Write an equation for the reverse reaction.

_____

c. Give the name of the type of reaction the forward change belongs to.

_____

d. Explain why an equilibrium cannot be established in an 'open system'.

_____

_____

 H **3.** The hydrogen for the Haber process can be obtained from methane by another reversible reaction. The formation of hydrogen is an endothermic process.

$$CH_4(g) \quad + \quad H_2O(g) \quad \rightleftharpoons \quad CO(g) + 3H_2(g)$$

a. What happens to the yield of hydrogen if the temperature is raised? Explain your answer.

_____

_____

_____

_____

_____

b. What happens to the yield of hydrogen if the pressure is increased? Explain your answer.

_____

_____

_____

_____

_____

Sciences   **CC13a Group 1**
Homework & skills

1. The following observations are made when the first three **group** 1 metals react with water.

Lithium	Sodium	Potassium
fizzes on the surface of the water	melts into a ball and fizzes about on the surface of the water	bursts into flames and flies about the surface of the water

Suggest what the reaction of water with the next group 1 metal, rubidium, would look like.

_____

_____

2. Write balanced equations with state symbols to show the reactions of rubidium with water and lithium with water.

_____

3. A small block of sodium is cut with a knife. Its shiny surface soon becomes dull.

a. Explain the changes that happen to the cut surface.

_____

_____

b. A small block of another metal in the same group is also cut. The cut surface of this metal becomes dull more slowly. Explain whether this metal would be found above or below sodium in the **periodic table**.

_____

_____

4. a. Complete this table.

Element	Atomic radius (nm)	Atomic number	Electronic configuration	Number of occupied electron shells
lithium	0.157			
sodium	0.191			
potassium	0.235	19		
rubidium	0.250	37	2.8.18.8.1	5
caesium	0.272	55	2.8.18.18.8.1	6

b. Explain why the atoms get larger as you go down the group.

_____

_____

c. Explain how the **reactivity** of the **alkali metals** is linked to their electronic configuration.

_____

_____

_____

Astatine is a **halogen** and is found below iodine in group 7 of the periodic table.

	Formula	Atomic number	Period number	Relative atomic mass	Melting point (°C)	Boiling point (°C)
chlorine	Cl	17	3	35.5	−101	−35
bromine	Br	35	4	80	−7	59
iodine	I	53	5	127	114	184
astatine	At	85	?	?	?	?

1. a. Describe the colour and state of each of the halogens chlorine, bromine and iodine.

_____

_____

b. Predict the colour and state of astatine.

_____

_____

2. Suggest the type of bonding found in astatine. _____

3. Write balanced equations with state symbols for the formation of the following ionic compounds.

a. silver(I) chloride, AgCl, from silver and chlorine

_____

b. aluminium bromide, $AlBr_3$, from aluminium and bromine.

_____

4. Describe the chemical test for chlorine gas.

_____

_____

5. Some information about the reactions and properties of halogens and their compounds is shown below.

	Chlorine	Bromine	Iodine
Reaction with zinc foil	burns quickly	glows brightly	glows dull red
Reaction with hydrogen	explodes in light	reacts when heated	reacts very slowly
Hydrogen halide solution	HCl(aq)	HBr(aq)	HI(aq)
pH (equal concentrations)	pH = 2.0	pH = 1.2	pH = 1.0

a. Write balanced equations with state symbols for the reactions of:

   i hydrogen and fluorine _____

   ii zinc and fluorine. _____

b. Predict what the reaction of fluorine with zinc foil would look like.

_____

c. **i** Name the acid formed when hydrogen fluoride dissolves in water. _____

   ii Write the formulae of the ions. _____

Sciences **CC14a** Rates of reaction

Marble chips (calcium carbonate) react with hydrochloric acid as follows.

calcium carbonate + hydrochloric acid → calcium chloride + water + carbon dioxide

One way to measure the **rate** of this reaction is to find the time taken to form 0.5 g of carbon dioxide.

The set-up for this investigation is shown opposite.

Two students carried out a series of reactions to see how changing the concentration of the hydrochloric acid, the surface area of the calcium carbonate (marble chips or powder) and the temperature of the reaction mixture affect the rate of reaction. Their results are shown in the table.

Note: The concentration of a solution is often given as the number of moles of solute dissolved in 1 dm^3 of solution. The unit is written as mol dm^{-3}. 1 dm^3 is the same volume as 1 litre or 1000 cm^3. The higher the number, the more concentrated the solution. **You do not need to remember the units for concentration.**

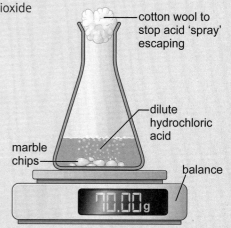

cotton wool to stop acid 'spray' escaping

dilute hydrochloric acid

marble chips

balance

Experiment	Concentration of hydrochloric acid (mol dm^{-3})	Temperature (°C)	Type of calcium carbonate	Time to make 0.5 g of carbon dioxide (s)
1	2.0	21	small chips	60
2	4.0	21	small chips	32
3	8.0	21	small chips	15
4	4.0	21	large chips	84
5	4.0	21	powder	4
6	2.0	33	small chips	28
7	2.0	42	small chips	13
8	2.0	50	small chips	7

1. State **two variables** that the students need to control, in all these experiments, to make the tests fair.

2. State the link between the time taken to produce 0.5 g of carbon dioxide gas and the reaction rate.

3. **a.** What is the effect of increasing the concentration of hydrochloric acid on the rate of reaction?

   b. Explain how the data in the table supports your answer to part **a**, by referring to specific results.

4. **a.** Which type of calcium carbonate used in these experiments has the biggest surface area?

   b. What is the effect of changing the surface area of calcium carbonate on the rate of reaction?

   c. Explain how the data in the table supports your answer to part **b**, by referring to specific results.

1. Read the paragraph below, then answer the questions that follow.

The catalytic converters in car exhausts contain millions of tiny pieces of platinum, rhodium and palladium spread over a honeycomb structure. When exhaust gases such as carbon monoxide (CO) and nitrogen dioxide (NO_2) pass over these metals, the metals act as a **catalyst** for the reactions that convert the exhaust gases into harmless gases including carbon dioxide (CO_2) and nitrogen (N_2).

a. Write a balanced equation for the conversion of carbon monoxide and nitrogen dioxide into carbon dioxide and nitrogen.

_____

b. Describe what a catalyst is and explain how it works in terms of changing the activation energy of a reaction.

_____

_____

_____

_____

_____

_____

_____

2. The results of an investigation into the decomposition of hydrogen peroxide using different metal oxides as catalysts are shown below.

a. Using the graph paper on the next page, plot the results on a chart or graph. Use the same axes for all the results. Time should be on the horizontal axis.

b. Rank the three catalysts in order of increasing effectiveness. Explain how you decided on your order.

Time (s)	Volume of oxygen formed with CuO catalyst (cm³)	Volume of oxygen formed with MnO₂ catalyst (cm³)	Volume of oxygen formed with ZnO catalyst (cm³)
0	0	0	0
20	2	10	0
40	4	19	0
60	5	27	0
80	7	33	0
100	8	39	0
120	9	44	0

_____

_____

_____

_____

_____

_____

c. List four variables that should be kept constant during the three experiments.

_____

_____

d. The students used a spatula to measure the same amount of solid metal oxide in each experiment. What could be done to improve the experiment instead of using a spatula?

_____

_____

_____

 3. The diagram on the right shows the **reaction profile** for a reaction carried out with an **enzyme** present.

a. Compare and contrast how enzymes and non-biological catalysts work.

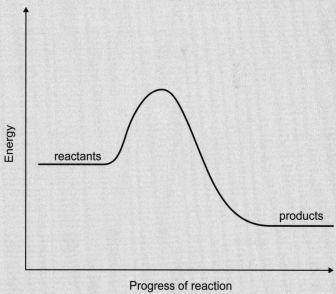

_____

_____

_____

_____

_____

_____

_____

b. Add a dotted line to the graph to represent the same reaction without the enzyme present.

c. Indicate and label the activation energy and overall energy change for each of the reactions on your graph.

d. Use the diagram to explain why the reaction is slower without the enzyme.

_____

_____

_____

1. Explain, in terms of energy transfers when bonds break and when bonds form, why the combustion of methane is an exothermic reaction.

_____

_____

2. Explain what is meant by the term '**activation energy**'.

_____

_____

3. This reaction between nitrogen and oxygen is endothermic: $N_2(g) + O_2(g) \rightarrow 2NO(g)$

Draw a **reaction profile** for the reaction, identifying the overall energy change and activation energy.

H The table shows some **bond energies**.

Covalent bond	C–O	C–C	C–H	H–H	O–H	O=O	C=C	C=O	C≡O
Bond energy (kJ mol^{-1})	336	347	413	436	464	498	612	805	1077

H **4.** Ethene reacts with hydrogen to produce ethane.

$$\underset{H}{\overset{H}{\diagdown}}C=C\underset{H}{\overset{H}{\diagup}} + H-H \longrightarrow H-\overset{\overset{H}{|}}{\underset{\underset{H}{|}}{C}}-\overset{\overset{H}{|}}{\underset{\underset{H}{|}}{C}}-H$$

a. Calculate the energy required to break all the bonds in the reactants.

_____

b. Calculate the energy released when all the bonds form in the products.

_____

c. Use your answers to parts **a** and **b** to calculate the overall energy change in the reaction.

_____

d. Explain what your answer to part **c** tells you about the reaction.

_____

_____

_____

Edexcel GCSE (9-1)

Sciences
Homework & skills

CC16a Hydrocarbons in crude oil
and natural gas

CC16 Fuels

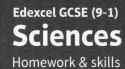

1. The diagram below shows the structures of four different compounds.

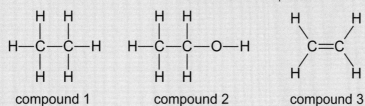

compound 1   compound 2   compound 3   compound 4

a. Identify which of these compounds (1, 2, 3 and 4) are **hydrocarbons**.

_____

b. Explain your answer to part **a**.

_____

_____

2. Describe the arrangements of the carbon atoms in the hydrocarbon molecules found in **crude oil**.

_____

_____

3. Explain why crude oil is described as a **finite resource**.

_____

_____

4. Fossil fuels are obtained from crude oil and **natural gas**.

a. Name **three** fossil fuels obtained from crude oil.

_____

b. Name the main fossil fuel obtained from natural gas.

_____

c. Explain why fossil fuels are described as **non-renewable**.

_____

_____

_____

d. Give **one** other way in which crude oil is an important source of useful substances.

_____

_____

_____

_____

Sciences
CC16c The alkane homologous series
Homework & skills

1. Ethanal is a member of a **homologous series** called the aldehydes. The table shows the **molecular formulae** of the first four aldehydes.

Name of aldehyde	methanal	ethanal	propanal	butanal
Molecular formula of aldehyde	CH_2O	C_2H_4O	C_3H_6O	C_4H_8O
Boiling point (°C)	−21	21	49	76

a. Describe **two** ways in which aldehyde molecules are similar to each other.

_____

_____

b. Describe how the molecular formulae of neighbouring aldehydes differ, going across the table.

_____

c. Describe how the boiling points of the aldehydes change as the number of carbon atoms in their molecules change.

_____

d. Ethanal can be oxidised to form ethanoic acid. Predict the name of the substance formed when butanal is oxidised.

_____

2. Octane is an **alkane** found in the 'petrol' crude oil fraction. The diagram shows its **structural formula**.

a. Give the molecular formula for octane.

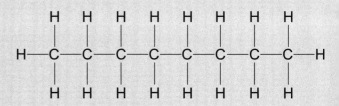

_____

b. Butane is an alkane found in the 'gases' crude oil fraction. Its molecular formula is C_4H_{10}. Draw the structural formula for butane.

 c. Pentacontane is an alkane found in the 'bitumen' crude oil fraction. Its molecules each contain 50 carbon atoms. Predict the molecular formula for pentacontane, and explain your answer.

_____

_____

_____

 d. The members of an homologous series show a gradual variation in physical properties.

  i Predict the order of the boiling points for octane, butane and pentacontane. Explain your answer.

_____

_____

_____

  ii Give **two** reasons that explain why these three compounds belong to the same homologous series.

_____

_____

_____

1. Explain why the combustion of some hydrocarbon fuels causes the production of sulfur dioxide.

_____

_____

2. Sulfur dioxide dissolves in rain water, forming **acid rain**.

a. Write a balanced equation for the reaction between sulfur dioxide and water to form sulfurous acid, H_2SO_3.

_____

b. Sulfurous acid reacts with oxygen in the air to form sulfuric acid, H_2SO_4.

    i Write a balanced equation for this reaction.

_____

    ii Explain how you know sulfurous acid is oxidised in this reaction.

_____

3. Oxides of nitrogen are **pollutants** formed during the use of fuels in engines.

a. State what is meant by a 'pollutant'.

_____

_____

b. Explain why oxides of nitrogen form in vehicle engines.

_____

_____

c. Nitrogen dioxide, NO_2, is an oxide of nitrogen. It is a common pollutant in areas with a lot of traffic.

Give one problem caused by nitrogen dioxide.

_____

_____

4. Acid rain contains sulfuric acid. This acid reacts with calcium carbonate, $CaCO_3$, a compound found in limestone and marble.

a. Write a balanced equation for the reaction between calcium carbonate and sulfuric acid.

_____

b. Describe why this reaction increases the rate of **weathering** of buildings made with these rocks.

_____

_____

5. Acid rain causes environmental problems. Explain **one** problem acid rain causes to:

a. plants on land

_____

b. animals in rivers and lakes

_____

c. metals, such as iron and steel, used for buildings.

_____

1. The graph shows how levels of oxygen may have changed during the history of the Earth's atmosphere.

a. What is responsible for the increase in oxygen levels in the atmosphere?

_____

_____

_____

_____

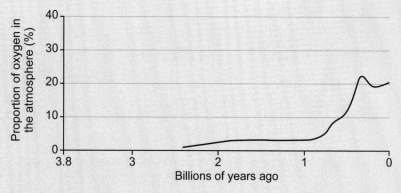

b. The first life may have evolved 3.7 billion years ago. Explain why this event did not affect the oxygen levels in the atmosphere at the time, even though this life consisted of **photosynthetic** microorganisms.

_____

c. Give a reason for why oxygen levels started to rise about 2.4 billion years ago.

_____

_____

2. The carbon cycle is the sequence of processes by which carbon moves from the atmosphere, through living and dead organisms, into sediments and back into the atmosphere. The diagram shows part of this cycle.

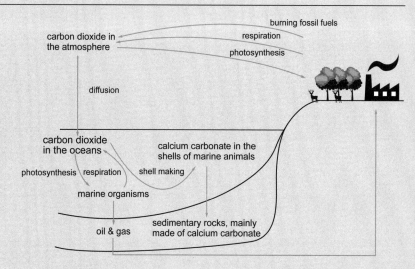

a. Explain why carbon dioxide levels in the Earth's early atmosphere fell after the oceans formed.

_____

_____

b. Explain how carbon dioxide was removed from the oceans 4 billion years ago.

_____

c. Explain how carbon dioxide is also removed from the oceans now.

_____

_____

d. Explain how carbon dioxide becomes permanently trapped underground.

_____

e. Explain how marine animals help to allow more carbon dioxide to be absorbed in the oceans.

_____

_____

H Venus, Earth and Mars are all rocky planets in our Solar System, but their atmospheres are very different. The pie charts below show the gases in their atmospheres.

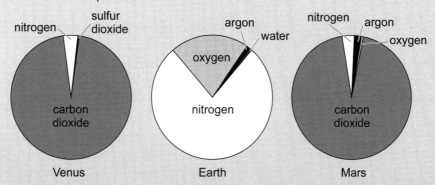

Venus is closer to the Sun than the Earth, and Mars is further away from the Sun than the Earth. Scientists can predict the temperature on the surface of each planet based on the amount of radiation it receives from the Sun, and how much of this is reflected by clouds in the atmosphere.

These predicted values are shown in the table. The predicted value for Venus is lower than that for the Earth because Venus is covered in clouds, which reflect sunlight.

Planet	Mass of atmosphere above 1 m² of the planet (kg)	Predicted surface temperature (°C)
Venus	1×10^6	−46
Earth	1×10^4	−18
Mars	2×10^2	−56

1. Explain which of the three planets you would expect to have the lowest surface temperature based on its position in the Solar System.

_____

_____

_____

2. The mean surface temperature of the Earth is about 33 °C higher than the predicted value.

a. Calculate the actual mean surface temperature of the Earth.

_____

b. Explain why the actual temperature is different from the predicted temperature.

_____

_____

c. One of the gases that can help to cause this effect is water vapour. Describe how **two** other gases, which help to cause this effect, are produced by human activities.

_____

_____

3. The actual surface temperature of Venus is about 500 °C higher than is predicted for the amount of solar radiation it receives. Suggest an explanation for why this difference is greater for Venus than for the Earth.

_____

_____

_____

_____

CC1 States of Matter

CC1a **States of matter**

Freeze-drying is used to prepare dehydrated foods such as instant coffee, pot snacks and powdered soup mixes. The food is cooled to between −50 °C and −80 °C, and then exposed to a very low air pressure. Under these conditions, any water in the food sublimates.

Explain, in terms of the arrangement and movement of water particles, the attractive forces between the particles, and energy transfers, why:

a. the food is first cooled down

_____

_____

_____

_____

_____

b. water in the food sublimates

_____

_____

_____

_____

_____

c. some heating is needed for sublimation to continue.

_____

_____

_____

_____

_____

CC2 Methods of Separating and Purifying Substances

CC2a **Mixtures**

During soldering, a mixture of metals ('solder') is heated until it melts. The molten metal falls into the gaps between two pieces of metal and freezes, joining the pieces of metal together. A 'soft solder' melts between 183 °C and 212 °C. A 'hard solder' melts between 620 °C and 680 °C.

Explain the difference in melting ranges. Explain in terms of the arrangement and movement of water particles, the attractive forces between them and energy transfers.

_____

_____

_____

CC3 Atomic Structure

CC3a Structure of an atom

Imagine that the nucleus of an atom is scaled up to be the size of this dot

Estimate the diameter of the atom, in relation to the size of this nucleus, by choosing one of the measurements below. Explain your choice.

1 mm	1 cm	1 m	1 km

CC3b Atomic number and mass number

Atoms contain three subatomic particles – protons, neutrons and electrons. The relative mass of a proton and a neutron is 1, while the mass of an electron can be regarded as negligible. The relative charge of a proton is +1 and that of an electron is –1.

a. Explain why the mass of an electron can be regarded as 'negligible'.

b. Explain what the final sentence tells us about the charges on a proton and an electron.

CC3c Isotopes

a. Naturally occurring silver has two isotopes: 51.9% is silver-107 and 48.1% is silver-109. Calculate the relative atomic mass of silver.

b. Silicon is made up of three isotopes: 92% is silicon-28; 5% is silicon-29 and 3% is silicon-30. Use this information to calculate the relative atomic mass of silicon.

c. Titanium has five common isotopes: ^{46}Ti (8.0%), ^{47}Ti (7.8%), ^{48}Ti (73.4%), ^{49}Ti (5.5%), ^{50}Ti (5.3%). What is the relative atomic mass of titanium?

CC4 The Periodic Table

CC4c Electronic configurations and the periodic table

In reactions, metal atoms can lose electrons and non-metal atoms can gain electrons. When this happens, charged particles called 'ions' form. Enough electrons are lost or gained so that the ion has the same electronic configuration as the nearest element in group 0.

For example:

- Sodium atoms (2.8.1) lose one electron to become sodium ions (2.8) – the same electronic configuration as neon in group 0.
- Sulfur atoms (2.8.6) gain two electrons to become sulfide ions (2.8.8) – the same electronic configuration as argon in group 0.

a. Work out how many electrons each atom in period 2 (Li to F) must lose or gain to obtain the same electronic configuration as the nearest group 0 element.

_____

_____

_____

_____

_____

_____

b. Describe how carbon and other elements in group 4 are unusual in the way they can form ions.

_____

_____

_____

CC5 Ionic Bonding

CC5a Ionic bonds

Describe, with the help of diagrams, how sodium oxide forms from sodium atoms and oxygen atoms.

```
┌─────────────────────────────────────────────────┐
│                                                 │
│                                                 │
│                                                 │
│                                                 │
│                                                 │
│                                                 │
│                                                 │
│                                                 │
│                                                 │
└─────────────────────────────────────────────────┘
```

CC5c Properties of ionic compounds

a. Calculate the number of electrons in the ions Na^+, Mg^{2+} and Al^{3+} (atomic numbers: Na = 11, Mg = 12, Al = 13).

_____

b. The melting point of potassium chloride is 770 °C and that of calcium oxide is 2614 °C. Suggest a reason why the melting point of calcium oxide is much higher than that of potassium chloride.

_____

_____

_____

_____

_____

CC6 Covalent Bonding

CC6a Covalent bonds

Find out about the bonding and structure of the fullerenes, forms of the element carbon.

a. What is the **molecular formula** for the first fullerene to be discovered, buckminsterfullerene?

_____

b. How many other atoms are joined to each carbon atom in buckminsterfullerene?

_____

c. Name **two** forms of carbon that do not exist as molecules.

_____

CC8 Acids and Alkalis

CC8a Acids, alkalis and indicators

We say that pH measurements obtained by using a pH meter are more accurate because they have greater **resolution** than those obtained using universal indicator.

Explain the meaning of the term '**resolution**' as it is used in the above sentence.

_____

_____

CC8e Alkalis and neutralisation

1. A student carries out a titration. This is the method she uses:

● put 25.0 cm³ of sodium hydroxide solution in a flask
● add dilute hydrochloric acid
● use a pH meter to measure and record the pH of the reaction mixture in the flask.

The table shows her results.

Volume of acid (cm³)	0.0	6.0	12.0	18.0	24.0	24.4	24.8	25.2	25.6	26.0	32.0	38.0	44.0	50.0
pH in the flask	12.9	12.6	12.5	12.1	11.2	11.0	10.5	3.5	3.0	2.8	2.0	1.8	1.7	1.5

a. Use the graph paper on the next page to plot a line graph to show her results:

● plot the volume of acid added in cm³ on the horizontal axis
● plot the pH of the mixture in the flask on the vertical axis
● draw a curve of best fit.

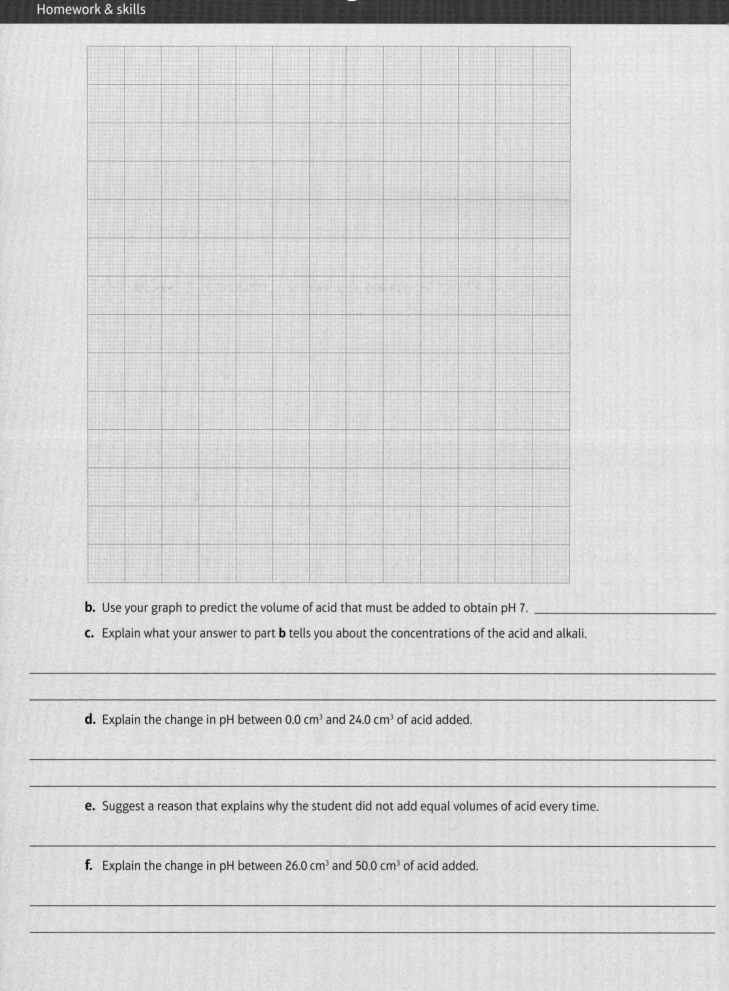

b. Use your graph to predict the volume of acid that must be added to obtain pH 7. _____

c. Explain what your answer to part **b** tells you about the concentrations of the acid and alkali.

_____

_____

d. Explain the change in pH between 0.0 cm^3 and 24.0 cm^3 of acid added.

_____

_____

e. Suggest a reason that explains why the student did not add equal volumes of acid every time.

_____

f. Explain the change in pH between 26.0 cm^3 and 50.0 cm^3 of acid added.

_____

_____

CC9 Calculations Involving Masses

CC9a Masses and empirical formula

1. A compound contains 70% iron and 30% oxygen. Calculate the empirical formula of this compound.

_____

2. Calculate the percentage of each element in potassium sulfate, K_2SO_4. Give your answer to 2 decimal places.

_____

CC9c Moles

1. A solution containing 9.8 g of sodium hydroxide was added to a solution containing 9.8 g sulfuric acid, H_2SO_4. The reaction taking place is

$$H_2SO_4 + 2NaOH \rightarrow Na_2SO_4 + 2H_2O$$

a. Calculate the number of moles of sodium hydroxide used.

_____

b. Calculate the number of moles of sulfuric acid used.

_____

c. Explain which of the reactants is the **limiting reactant**.

_____

_____

_____

_____

d. Calculate the maximum mass of sodium sulfate that could be produced in this reaction.

_____

CC10 Electrolytic Processes

CC10a **Electrolysis**

 H Molten aluminium oxide, containing Al^{3+} and O^{2-} ions, is electrolysed to produce molten aluminium and oxygen gas.

a. Write the half equation for the reaction occurring at the **anode**. Include state symbols.

b. Write the half equation for the reaction occurring at the **cathode**. Include state symbols.

c. Write the overall equation for the decomposition of aluminium oxide.

CC11 Obtaining and Using Metals

CC11a **Reactivity**

 H Zinc reacts with copper nitrate solution.

$$Zn + Cu(NO_3)_2 \rightarrow Zn(NO_3)_2 + Cu$$

a. Write the ionic equation for this reaction.

b. State what is meant by a **spectator ion**.

c. Write the **two half equations** for this reaction.

d. Explain what has been oxidised and what has been reduced in this reaction.

CC12 Reversible Reactions and Equilibria

CC12a **Dynamic equilibrium**

Complete the flow diagram to show what happens in the Haber process.

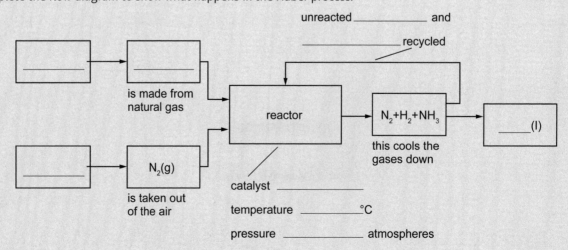

CC13 Groups in the Periodic Table

CC13a Group 1

The melting points of these alkali metals are:

	Lithium	Sodium	Potassium	Rubidium	Caesium
melting point (°C)	181	98	64		28

Predict the melting point of rubidium. Explain how you worked out your prediction.

_____

_____

_____

_____

CC13b Group 7

The table shows halogens and their properties.

	Formula	Atomic number	Period number	Relative atomic mass	Melting point (°C)	Boiling point (°C)
chlorine	Cl	17	3	35.5	−101	−34
bromine	Br	35	4	80	−7	59
iodine	I	53	5	127	114	184
astatine	At	85	?	?	?	?

1. Using the graph paper on the following page and only the data for chlorine, bromine and iodine, draw scatter graphs of boiling point (vertical axis) against:

a. period in the periodic table   **b.** atomic number.

2. The boiling point of astatine is usually reported as 337 °C. Using the two graphs from question **1**, compare and contrast the predicted value(s) of the boiling point of astatine with the reported value.

_____

_____

CC14 Rates of Reaction

CC14a **Rates of reaction**

 1. Write a balanced equation for the reaction between hydrochloric acid and calcium carbonate. The equation should show that 2 mol of hydrochloric acid produces 1 mol of carbon dioxide gas.

_____

_____

 2. When 5 mol of hydrochloric acid are reacted with excess calcium carbonate, calculate the number of moles of each of the following: calcium chloride, water and carbon dioxide.

_____

CC14c **Catalysts and activation energy**

1. Metal structures can be protected by the addition of substances that slow corrosion. For example, the addition of zinc phosphate to paint can slow the corrosion of steel. These substances are called inhibitors or, sometimes, negative catalysts.

a. Suggest how inhibitors may work.

_____

_____

_____

_____

b. Suggest **one** other possible use for an inhibitor.

_____

_____

_____

CC15 Heat Energy Changes in Chemical Reactions
CC15b **Energy changes in reactions**

 H The table shows some information about the complete combustion of three alcohols.

Alcohol	Equation for complete combustion	Energy change in reaction (kJ mol⁻¹)
methanol	$CH_3OH + 1\frac{1}{2}O_2 \rightarrow CO_2 + 2H_2O$	to be calculated
ethanol	$C_2H_5OH + 3O_2 \rightarrow 2CO_2 + 3H_2O$	−1298
propanol	$C_3H_7OH + 4\frac{1}{2}O_2 \rightarrow 3CO_2 + 4H_2O$	−1916

a. Calculate the overall energy change in the combustion of methanol.

_____

b. Predict the overall energy change in the combustion of butanol, C_4H_9OH, and explain your answer.

_____

_____

_____

_____

_____

CC16 Fuels

CC16c **The alkane homologous series**

The table shows the densities of the first eight straight-chain alkanes at room temperature and pressure.

Alkane	No. of carbon atoms	Density (kg/m³)	Alkane	No. of carbon atoms	Density (kg/m³)
methane	1	0.654	pentane	5	626
ethane	2	1.22	hexane	6	660
propane	3	1.80	heptane	7	684
butane	4	2.37	octane	8	703

a. None of these alkanes exist as solids at room temperature and pressure. Explain, in terms of the arrangement of particles, how the data shows evidence that some of these alkanes exist as liquids and some as gases at room temperature and pressure.

_____

_____

b. Explain how the data shows evidence that the alkanes form an homologous series.

_____

_____

Sciences
CP1a Vectors and scalars
Homework & skills

1. Al and Ben started at A and travelled north to B. Then they turned east and went to C, then south to D and then travelled east back to A. The **distance** in a straight line between A and C is 500 m.

Describe the distance they have travelled and their **displacement** from A when they reach the following points. The first one has been done for you.

a. point B

distance = 300 m, displacement = 300 m north of A

b. point C

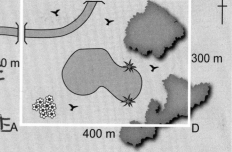

distance = 700m, displacement = 500m N|E

c. point D

distane = 1000m, displacement = 400m Eₐ

d. point A

distance = 300m, displacement = 300 m N

2. Al walked at a constant **speed** of 1.5 m/s between A and B. Ben jogged at a **velocity** of 3 m/s northwards from A to B.

Describe their velocities for the rest of their journey if they both maintained the speed at which they started.

Ben speed was faster because he was jogging instead of walking.

3. Car X drives north at 30 km/h. Car Y drives south at 30 km/h. Explain which of these things are the same for both cars after one hour.

- speed
- velocity
- distance travelled
- displacement

4. A maze is set out in a grid pattern, with all the corners right angles. This means that all the paths in this maze go north, south, east or west. A person in the maze follows the path described on the right.

> 3 m north, 2 m west, 1 m south, 1 m west, 2 m north, 6 m east, 2 m north

a. What is her final displacement in a north/south direction? _____

b. What is her final displacement in an east/west direction? _____

c. What is the total distance travelled? _____

1. Work out the missing value for each bicycle, and describe in words what is happening to the bicycle.

 velocity

velocity

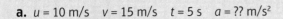

a. $u = 10$ m/s $v = 15$ m/s $t = 5$ s $a = ??$ m/s²

b. $u = 12$ m/s $v = 6$ m/s $t = ??$ s $a = -3$ m/s²

c. $u = 12.5$ m/s $v = ??$ m/s $t = 3$ s $a = -2.5$ m/s²

d. $u = ??$ m/s $v = 11$ m/s $t = 4.5$ s $a = -2$ m/s²

2. a. A dog chasing a cat accelerates from rest at 2 m/s². How long will it take the dog to reach a velocity of 10 m/s?

$$A = (v2 - v1)/T = (10 - 2)/4$$

b. The cat starts at a velocity of 5 m/s. It accelerates at 1.5 m/s² for 3 s. What is its final velocity? $8/4 = 2m/s$

$4.5 m/s$

3. A ball dropped from a sixth floor window accelerates at 10 m/s². After 2 seconds it hits the ground. It bounces back with a velocity of −15 m/s.

a. What is the symbol used to represent the acceleration due to gravity?

b. What is the ball's velocity when it hits the ground?   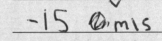 -15 $0 m/s$

c. What is meant by a velocity of −15 m/s?

That is going 15 m/s slower

d. What is the change in velocity of the ball when it bounces?

It goes up

e. The ball is in contact with the ground for 0.2 s when it bounces. What is its mean acceleration while it is in contact with the ground?

The ball is fotlng

4. Use the information in question **2** and your answers to work out how far the dog and the cat travel while they are accelerating.

$v^2 - u^2 = 2 \times a \times x$

$$A = (v2 - v1)/T = (10 - 2)/4$$
$$8/4 = 2m/s$$

$$v^2 - u^2 = 2 \times a \times x$$

Sciences CP2b Newton's First Law

Homework & skills

1. For each scenario, say what the direction of the resultant force is and what the effect on the object will be.

a. A bag of shopping weighs 50 N. There is a force of 60 N upwards.

upwards, also the bag will be lighter ✓

b. A boy kicks a ball. His foot pushes forward with 18 N. Friction pushes back with 3 N.

forwards, and the ball we be slightly slower ✓

c. A moving skateboarder drags her foot on the ground making a force of friction.

The Skateboard is slowing down Slowly ✓

d. A fish swims against a current. The current has a backwards force of 8 N. The fish's tail pushes forward with a force of 8 N.

equal, the forces will be equal ✓

e. A boy strikes a snooker ball with a cue. The force from the cue is 20 N. The force of friction from the table is 4 N.

forwards, the ball we go 4n slower than before ✓

f. A car engine is providing a forwards force of 750 N. The force of air resistance is 150 N and the friction on the road provides a force of 100 N.

forward, the car will go 250 n slower than before ✓

2. The diagram shows the forces acting on an aeroplane in flight. A decrease in speed of the aeroplane will reduce the lift (upwards force) produced by the wings while an increase in speed will increase the lift.

a. What is the resultant force on the plane? (include its size and direction in your answer)

the are equal at 1500N

b. Explain the effect this resultant force will have on the motion of the aeroplane.

The plane will stay the same Speed.

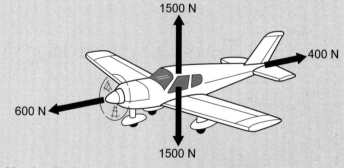

1500 N

400 N

600 N

1500 N

H 3. When an aeroplane turns it needs to fly at an angle like this. Explain why this is necessary.

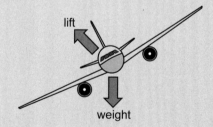

lift

weight

Because at plane cant turn like a car it has to turn at an angle because there is air resents.

Sciences CP2d Newton's Second Law
Homework & skills

1. For each object:
   - calculate the size and direction of the resultant force
   - calculate the size of its acceleration and state the direction.

| 1 tonne = 1000 kg |

a.

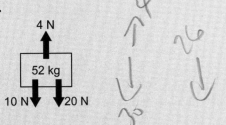

4 N

52 kg

10 N 20 N

_____26 N_____

b.

4 N
8 N
3 N 1 tonne 3 N 6N
8 N
6 N 10 N

_____16N_____

2. Complete the table below by calculating the missing values.

Object	Force (N)	Mass (kg)	Acceleration (m/s²)
sprinter	~~78~~ 160	80	2 m\s
charging elephant	1000	1000	~~1000~~ 1000 m\s
racing car	~~4er~~ 4500	500	9 m\s
cyclist	150	~~140~~ 100	1.5 m\s
bullet	80	0.002	40,000 m\s
hockey ball	4	~~260~~ 0.13	30 m\s

Remember the units must always be kilograms, seconds and metres.

1 kg = 1000 g
1 km/h = 0.28 m/s

3. A golf ball has a mass of 45 g. In a speed test, a golf ball was driven from rest to a velocity of 90 m/s.

45-90 =
4 S

a. If the time taken for the golf ball to reach this velocity was 0.0005 seconds, what acceleration was this?

f 180,00
0.0005 -45 = 0.0045

b. What force was applied to the golf ball?

_____0.0005_____

4. A supertanker carrying oil has a mass of 300 000 tonnes. By using its engines in reverse, a tanker like this can stop from a speed of 22 km/h in 14 minutes.

a. What acceleration is this?

_____221 km\h_____

b. What force is required?

_____thrust_____

H 5. a. What does **inertial mass** mean?

_____

_____

b. How does the inertial mass of an object compare to its mass found using its weight and the gravitational field strength?

_____

_____

H **1.** Use the idea of **conservation of momentum** to explain why a golf ball leaves the surface of a golf club at a much greater velocity than the club was moving before it hit the ball.

_____

_____

_____

H **2.** A trolley of mass 0.5 kg is moving down a ramp at a constant velocity of 3 m/s. When it is half-way down the ramp a lump of modelling clay of mass 0.1 kg is dropped on the trolley. The clay sticks to the trolley and they move off together with a new common velocity.

a. What is the **momentum** of the trolley before the clay is added?

_____

b. What is the momentum of the trolley and clay after the impact?

_____

c. Calculate the common velocity of the trolley and clay after impact.

_____

H **3.** A skater of mass 75 kg moving at 5 m/s takes hold of a stationary skater of mass 55 kg. Both skaters move off together after the collision. Calculate the velocity of the skaters after the collision.

_____

H **4.** A marble of mass 10 g moving at 1 m/s hits a stationary marble of mass 5 g. The 10 g marble continues to move at a velocity of 0.4 m/s after the collision. Calculate the velocity of the 5 g marble after the collision.

> Remember to convert all masses to kilograms before carrying out any calculations.

_____

H **5.** A 10 kg trolley (A) is moving due west at 5 m/s in a straight line. Describe movement to the west as movement in the positive direction. A second trolley of mass 15 kg (B) is travelling in the same straight line but due east at 10 m/s. The two trolleys collide, stick together and move off with a common velocity. Calculate this final velocity. Show all your working.

_____

Sciences
CP2h Crash hazards

Homework & skills

The manufacturers of this car have asked their design team to develop a new model.

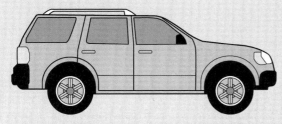

Some of the suggested changes are:

- use lighter materials to reduce the mass of the car
- fit brakes that can produce a greater braking force
- increase the force the engine can produce
- make the bonnet longer without increasing the size of the engine
- fit airbags in the driver and passenger doors
- lower the roof slightly to give it a more streamlined shape.

These changes will affect the performance of the car (its acceleration and braking), and some will also affect its safety.

1. If there are no other changes, explain what effect reducing the mass of the car will have on:

a. its acceleration when starting to move

_____

_____

b. its stopping distance at a particular speed

_____

_____

_____

H c. the force on it in a collision.

_____

_____

_____

2. Explain which other factors will affect:

a. its acceleration when starting to move

_____

_____

_____

H b. its stopping distance at a particular speed.

_____

_____

_____

3. What effect(s) will increasing the bonnet length have on the force in a collision? Explain your answer, including any assumptions you made.

_____

_____

_____

_____

_____

_____

_____

Hot water in homes is normally provided by a gas boiler. However, many houses have immersion heaters in their hot water tanks that use electricity to heat the water. Immersion heaters are used if the home has no gas supply, or if the central heating is switched off for the summer. A more efficient way of heating water is to use a heat pump. This acts a little bit like a fridge in reverse – it takes warm air from the house and 'concentrates' the energy to heat water. This works even in the winter, although then the water sometimes needs a bit of extra heating from an immersion heater.

A

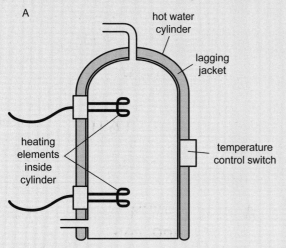

B

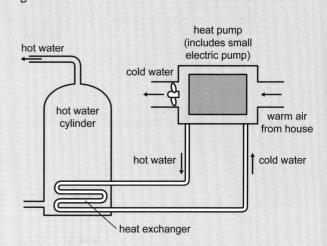

It takes 1.2 kilowatt hours (kWh) of electrical energy to heat a tank full of water using a heat pump. It takes 5.5 kWh if the same amount of water is heated using an immersion heater. A kilowatt hour is a unit of energy used by energy suppliers. (1 kWh = 3 600 000 J)

1. The immersion heater and hot water cylinder together (diagram A) have an **efficiency** of 0.73.

a. How much energy is transferred to the water in the cylinder?

_____

b. How is the wasted energy transferred?

_____

H **c.** How could the efficiency of the immersion heater and its cylinder be increased?

_____

_____

2. a. How is wasted energy transferred by the heat pump (diagram B)? (*Hint*: there is more than one way.)

_____

_____

b. The heat pump transfers the same amount of useful energy to the water in the tank as the immersion heater. Calculate its efficiency based on the energy used by the motor. (*Hint*: your answer may look wrong to you!)

_____

1. Small birds often look bigger when the weather is cold because they fluff their feathers up. Suggest why they do this.

_____

_____

2. Many houses have double-glazed windows. These have two sheets of glass with an air gap between them. Why does double glazing provide better **insulation** than single glazing?

_____

_____

3. First aiders will often cover someone who has been injured outdoors with a very thin blanket made from shiny metal foil. Suggest some of the advantages and disadvantages of using foil instead of a normal blanket.

_____

_____

_____

_____

_____

The diagram shows different ways of making a house more energy efficient.

4. Explain what energy efficient means when we are talking about a house.

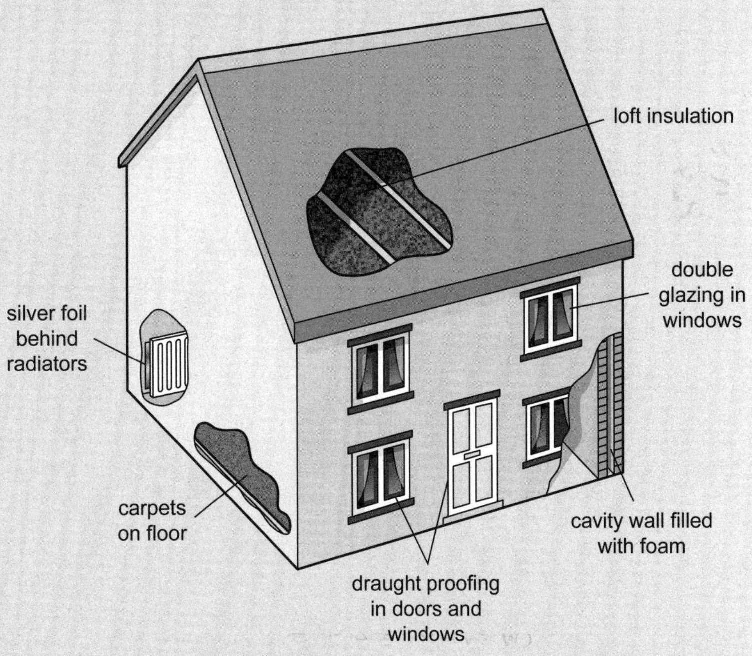

_____

_____

_____

_____

_____

loft insulation

double glazing in windows

silver foil behind radiators

cavity wall filled with foam

carpets on floor

draught proofing in doors and windows

5. Explain how each of the labelled features helps to make the house on the right more energy efficient. Use the phrase '**thermal conductivity**' in at least two of your explanations.

_____

_____

_____

_____

_____

_____

_____

Pollution-free motoring!

The new *Zap!* car has batteries instead of a fuel tank. Just plug in for a couple of hours and you are set for miles of pollution-free motoring! No carbon-dioxide emissions!

Our electric car has an efficiency of 0.75 compared with only around 0.15 for a petrol-driven car.

1. Electric cars use energy stored in a battery.

a. Explain why electricity is not considered to be an energy resource.

_____

_____

b. Explain why the statement that the electric car provides 'pollution-free motoring' is misleading.

_____

_____

2. Most cars use petrol or diesel as energy stores.

a. Describe **two** advantages of these fuels when used in cars.

_____

_____

b. Describe **one** disadvantage shared by all uses of **fossil fuels**.

_____

3. An electric car **can** be run without causing the emission of polluting gases. Explain how this can be done.

_____

_____

_____

4. The efficiency of the *Zap!* car is given as 0.75. What does this mean?

_____

5. Power stations can be fitted with scrubbers that remove waste gases. Carbon dioxide captured in this way can be stored underground instead of being released into the atmosphere.

If an electric car has the same overall efficiency as a petrol car, explain how using the electric car instead of the petrol car **could** help to reduce the amount of carbon dioxide being put into the atmosphere.

_____

_____

_____

Edexcel GCSE (9-1)
Sciences
CP4b Wave speeds
Homework & skills

1. A longitudinal seismic wave travels through 2 km of granite in 2.5 s. Calculate the speed of the wave.

_____

2. A transverse seismic wave travels at 3000 m/s in rock. How long will it take this wave to travel 10 km?

_____

3. The call of a whale has a frequency of 30 Hz. Sound travels at a velocity of around 1500 m/s in sea water.

a. Calculate the wavelength of the sound waves.

_____

b. How far will the sound travel in 5 minutes?

_____

4. A hunter fires a gun and hears an echo from a cliff face 5 s later. He knows the cliff is 850 m away. How fast is the sound travelling back to where the hunter is?

_____

5. A tsunami is a wave caused when a landslide falls into the sea, or when there is an earthquake on the sea bed. A tsunami off the coast of Japan can travel 8600 km to the coast of California in 17 hours.

a. Calculate the velocity of the tsunami wave.

_____

b. How long would it take a similar wave to travel from Sumatra to Sri Lanka (a distance of approximately 1500 km)?

_____

6. Light waves are part of a family of waves (called electromagnetic waves) that all travel at 3×10^8 m/s when travelling through a vacuum.

The table shows some typical frequencies or wavelengths for the different parts of the electromagnetic spectrum.

Calculate the missing values in the table.

Name of wave	Frequency (Hz)	Wavelength (m)
a radio		100
b microwaves	3×10^{10}	
c visible light		1×10^6
d infrared	3×10^{12}	
e ultraviolet		1×10^7
f X-rays	3×10^{19}	

Material	Speed of light (m/s)
vacuum	3×10^8
air	3×10^8
glass	2×10^8
water	2.25×10^8
diamond	1.24×10^8

The table shows the speed of light in different materials. You may need to use this information to help you to answer some of the questions below.

H **1.** Light is refracted when its speed changes. This usually happens because it has travelled into a different medium.

a. Does light bend towards the normal when it speeds up or when it slows down?
Explain your answer, using information from the table.

_____

_____

_____

b. Put the pairs of materials below into order, starting with the one in which light will be refracted by the smallest angle. Explain how you worked out your answer.

- air → glass
- air → diamond
- glass → water
- glass → diamond

_____

_____

_____

_____

H **2.** When light goes from one medium to another, its frequency does not change. The wavelength of red light travelling in a vacuum is 700 nm (1 nm = 1×10^{-9} m). Calculate the wavelength of this light in:

a. glass

_____

b. water

_____

c. diamond.

_____

The diagram shows how the atmosphere absorbs or transmits different parts of the **electromagnetic spectrum**.

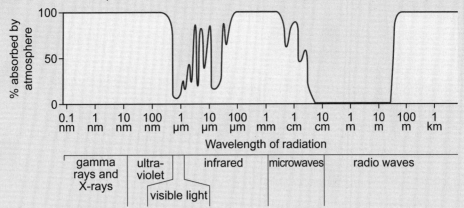

 1. Gamma ray telescopes can be used on Earth.

a. Explain why Earth-based gamma ray telescopes are located on the tops of mountains.

_____

_____

_____

b. Explain one advantage and one disadvantage of using a gamma ray telescope on a satellite.

_____

_____

_____

_____

_____

c. Suggest **one** other type of telescope that is best located in space.

_____

_____

_____

_____

2. The diagram shows the wavelengths in nm, μm, mm, cm, m and km.
Give the full name for each of these units.

_____

_____

_____

 3. The numbers on the diagram can all be expressed in metres, using numbers in standard form. For example, 1 nm = 1×10^{-9} m, and 10 cm = 1×10^{-1} m. Give the following lengths in metres and standard form.

a. 100 nm _____

b. 1 μm _____

c. 10 μm _____

d. 1 km _____

1. Read the following story.

Cyril's magazine had an interesting story about a radio telescope looking for possible signals from aliens. He put the magazine down to get his porridge out of the microwave. At the same time the toaster popped up. His toast was burnt again. He switched off the radio and took his breakfast into the living room to watch TV.

He pressed the remote to switch on. There was a news report from the USA, live by satellite. Cyril shivered with the cold and switched the electric fire on. He could feel the warmth as soon as he pressed the switch.

Identify the different parts of the electromagnetic spectrum mentioned in the story, and how each is being used.

_____

_____

_____

_____

_____

_____

_____

_____

_____

_____

2. Describe **one** use not mentioned in the story for:

a. visible light _____

b. infrared _____

c. microwaves _____

Communications can be sent by radio waves and microwaves. Optical fibres can also be used to send communications signals using visible light. The equation triangle on the right shows the relationship between speed, distance and time.

3. How long would it take a radio signal to travel 50 km?

_____

4. How much longer would it take to send the same signal using optical fibres?

$x = $ distance, $v = $ speed, $t = $ time

speed of light in air = 3×10^8 m/s

speed of light in glass = 2×10^8 m/s

_____

_____

Ⓗ **5.** Describe how radio waves are:

a. produced _____

b. detected. _____

A doctor's diary

> Called to A & E department to look at an X-ray of a toddler. Parents thought she had swallowed something she should not have. Sure enough, several white circles showed against the greyer outlines of her spine and pelvis. Coins, most likely, that will reappear naturally in a day or so. But also a fainter image of what looked like a plastic brick.
>
> Gamma scans: man with treated cancer in for a follow-up check. No concentrations of radiation detected, so he is probably clear – good news!

1. Explain why X-rays are used, rather than ultraviolet or visible light, to take images of the inside of the body.

_____

_____

2. Explain what the description of the toddler's X-ray tells you about the ways that the following materials transmit or absorb X-rays.

a. muscle and other soft tissues _____

_____

b. bone _____

_____

c. metal _____

_____

d. plastic _____

_____

3. a. How is a gamma scan carried out?

_____

_____

b. How is this different from the way an X-ray is carried out?

_____

_____

c. What do X-rays and gamma rays have in common that makes them useful for medical imaging?

_____

_____

H d. Materials in the body affect gamma rays and X-rays differently. Describe the differences.

_____

_____

97

Sciences
CP6a Atomic models
Homework & skills

1. Describe the plum pudding model of the **atom**.

_____

_____

2. These diagrams show three different models of the atom.

A   B   C

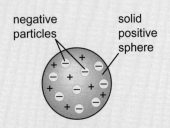

negative particles   solid positive sphere

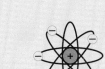

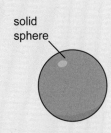

solid sphere

The bullet points below give some information about the different models.

- Ernest Rutherford carried out experiments to investigate the structure of the atom.
- J.J. Thompson suggested the plum pudding model of the atom in 1904.
- John Dalton suggested his model of the atom in 1805. It has sometimes been called a billiard ball model.
- Rutherford's model describes atoms as consisting of …
- Rutherford's model explains the results of the alpha-scattering experiments by saying that …
- Rutherford's team fired alpha particles at thin gold foil, and found that …
- The plum pudding model describes an atom as …
- This model explained how **electrons** might be part of the atom.
- This model helped scientists to explain some of the properties of matter.

Put the sentences in the bullet points into a sensible order and use them to help you to write one or two paragraphs to describe how and why the atomic model has changed over time.

A good answer will link ideas in a sensible order and use correct grammar, spelling and punctuation. You can change the wording in the bullet points if you wish.

_____

_____

_____

_____

_____

_____

_____

_____

_____

_____

_____

_____

_____

_____

Sciences
CP6b Inside atoms
Homework & skills

1. a. Complete the table using information from diagrams A and B.

Atom	No. of protons	No. of neutrons	No. of electrons
A			
B			

b. What are the similarities between these two atoms?

_____

c. What are the differences between these two atoms?

_____

_____

d. Are they **isotopes**? Explain your answer.

_____

_____

_____

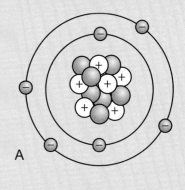

A

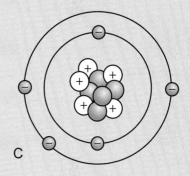

B

2. a. Complete the table using information from diagrams C and D.

Atom	No. of protons	No. of neutrons	No. of electrons
C			
D			

b. What are the similarities between these two atoms?

_____

_____

c. What are the differences between these two atoms?

_____

_____

_____

d. Are they isotopes? Explain your answer.

_____

_____

_____

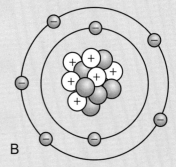

C

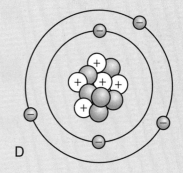

D

3. Write each of the following in symbols, in the form $^A_Z X$.

a. beryllium-9, which has four **protons** _____

b. phosphorus-31, which has a **proton number** of 15 _____

c. argon, which has a **nucleon number** of 40 and 22 **neutrons** _____

d. aluminium, which has a nucleon number of 27 and 14 neutrons _____

e. potassium, which has 19 protons and 20 neutrons _____

f. magnesium, which has 12 protons and 12 neutrons _____

Scientists assume that there is no safe level of radioactivity. Even low amounts of ionising radiation carry some risk. One way of deciding whether this risk is significant is to compare the level of radiation from a source with the **background radiation**. We are constantly exposed to radioactive material. Our food, the air and our homes all give out ionising radiation. We also receive ionising radiation from outer space in the form of **cosmic rays**. About 100 cosmic rays pass through you each second.

The amount of ionising radiation that people are exposed to varies from place to place. In the UK, background radiation levels are highest in Yorkshire, Aberdeen, Devon and Cornwall. This is related to the rocks in these areas. Most of the radioactivity in rocks comes from the radioactive isotopes uranium-238 and thorium-232. Different rock types have different amounts of uranium-238 and thorium-232.

Radioactivity in the air comes from radon gas, which is produced when uranium-238 decays. When we breathe in radon gas, the radon may emit alpha particles in our lungs. When ionising radiation from a source reaches our body, our cells can be damaged by it.

When radioactive material touches our skin, is eaten or is breathed in, our bodies absorb the radioactive material. When radioactive materials dissolve in water, plants take them up and they may become part of the food chain. Foods and drinks that contain radioactive materials include tea, coffee and Brazil nuts. As we ingest radioactive materials, we are all slightly radioactive.

1. Is there such a thing as a safe level of radiation? Explain your answer.

_____

2. How do scientists decide whether a level of ionising radiation is significant?

_____

3. Is the average amount that each person receives in the UK a safe level of radiation? Explain your answer.

_____

_____

4. Name **three** sources of background radiation.

_____

5. a What are cosmic rays?

_____

b. Do you think the number of cosmic rays passing through the body is the same for every person? Explain your answer.

_____

_____

6. Which places in the UK have the highest background radiation levels?

7. What produces natural background radiation on Earth?

8. Explain in your own words what the final sentence of the passage above means.

_____

_____

You will need a copy of the periodic table to help you answer some of these questions.

1. a. Describe how α radiation is similar to β^- radiation.

_____

b. What are the key differences between α radiation and β^- radiation?

_____

_____

2. Why do we refer to α particles and β particles, but not γ particles?

_____

_____

3. How does γ radiation compare with both α and β radiation in terms of:

a. ionising capabilities _____

b. penetration _____

c. mass _____

d. charge? _____

4. Uranium-238 undergoes α decay. What effect does α radiation have on:

a. the proton number (the charge on the nucleus) _____

b. the mass number? _____

5. Nickel-60 undergoes γ decay. What effect does this have on:

a. the proton number _____

b. the mass number? _____

6. What effect does emitting a neutron $\left(^{1}_{0}n\right)$ have on:

a. the proton number _____

b. the mass number? _____

7. What effect does β^- decay have on:

a. the proton number _____

b. the mass number? _____

8. What new element forms when uranium-238 emits an alpha particle? _____

9. Write balanced **nuclear equations** to explain what happens when:

a. francium-211 $\left(^{211}_{87}Fr\right)$ decays to astatine-207 $\left(^{207}_{85}At\right)$ _____

b. beryllium-13 $\left(^{13}_{9}Be\right)$ emits a neutron _____

c. iron-59 $\left(^{59}_{26}Fe\right)$ undergoes β^- decay. _____

Sciences
CP6h Dangers of radioactivity
Homework & skills

You do not need to remember the details on this sheet for your exam, but you could be asked to apply your knowledge to unfamiliar situations.

Sellafield is on the coast of Cumbria. It is where the UK's first nuclear power stations were built, and now deals with used nuclear fuel. The first nuclear reactors at Sellafield were at part of the site called Calder Hall. Two reactors were also built to make plutonium to use in nuclear weapons. These were called the Windscale piles.

In 1957, there was a fire in one of the Windscale piles, which is still the worst nuclear accident in the UK. The fire spread radioactive **contamination** across Europe. One of the most concerning isotopes to be released was iodine-131, which can lead to thyroid cancer. Other isotopes released included caesium-137 and xenon-133. The amounts of these isotopes released were a lot smaller than the quantities released by the disasters at Chernobyl and Fukushima, but they were still a cause for concern. Milk from the area was dumped into the Irish Sea for a month after the accident. None of the workers involved in the clean-up appeared to have any long-term health effects according to a study in 2010, but it is estimated that the fire may have resulted in over 200 additional cases of cancer.

Cumbria also suffered the effects of contamination after the Chernobyl disaster in 1986. Chernobyl is in the Ukraine, over 2000 km from Cumbria. Radioactive isotopes were washed out of the atmosphere by the rain, and a lot of the radioactive rain fell on Cumbria. Sheep farming is the main form of agriculture in much of Cumbria, and following the accident sheep farmers were forbidden to move their animals around, and had to have them tested for radiation before they could be sold. These restrictions also affected parts of Scotland and Wales, and were only completely lifted in 2012.

1. a. Explain the difference in meaning between the terms 'irradiation' and 'contamination'.

_____

_____

b. People affected by the Windscale fire included workers at the site and the surrounding population. Explain which of these groups might have been affected by irradiation.

_____

_____

_____

2. a. Explain how milk could have become radioactive after the Windscale accident.

_____

_____

b. Explain whether this is an example of irradiation or contamination.

_____

_____

3. a. Explain how the meat in sheep became radioactive after the Chernobyl accident.

_____

_____

b. Suggest why the restrictions on sheep lasted for over 25 years, but after the Windscale fire milk was discarded for only around a month.

_____

_____

c. Explain why it was considered unsafe to eat sheep from Cumbria, but safe to handle them on the farm.

_____

_____

_____

Sciences
CP7a Work and power
Homework & skills

1. Sam and Joe climb 6 m up into a tree. Sam uses a rope to pull up his bag with their lunch in it.

a. Sam's weight is 550 N. How much work does he do when he climbs the tree?

_____

b. Sam's bag weighs 20 N. How much work does he do when he pulls the bag up?

_____

c. Sam and Joe are the same weight. Joe climbs the tree faster than Sam. Explain who has exerted the greater **power**.

_____
_____
_____

d. It takes Sam 5 seconds to pull his bag up. How much power has he used?

_____

2. Jen pushes a crate along the floor with a force of 50 N. She does work of 450 N.

a. How far did she push the crate?

_____

b. Jen's power was 25 W. How long did it take her to push the crate?

_____

3. The diagram shows a ramp leading to a platform. A worker has to move a heavy suitcase from the floor to the top of the platform.

platform

a. Describe how to calculate the **work done** if the person lifts the suitcase vertically upwards to put it on the platform.

_____

b. In theory the person needs to use less force if she pushes the suitcase up the ramp. Explain why the work done should be the same as if she lifts it directly.

_____
_____

c. In fact, the work done to push the suitcase up the ramp may be a little more than that needed to lift it directly. Suggest a reason for this.

_____
_____

Sciences **CP8b** Vector diagrams
Homework & skills

1. The diagram on the right is a **free body force diagram** showing one of the forces on a submarine. The submarine is travelling at a steady speed. The upthrust and weight are balanced and are much larger than the force from the engines.

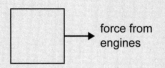

a. Complete the diagram and add the missing arrows and labels.

b. Explain how the diagram would be different if the submarine were accelerating.

_____

_____

_____

2. The diagram on the right shows a person pushing a loaded suitcase up a ramp. The top of the platform is 1.5 m above the ground, and the ramp is 4.4 m long at an angle of 20° to the ground. The weight of the loaded suitcase is 800 N.

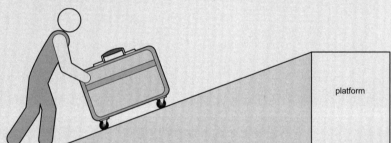

a. Calculate the work done if a weight of 800 N is raised vertically from the ground to the top of the platform. The weight of the suitcase acts vertically downwards.

_____

b. The weight of the suitcase acts vertically downwards. Draw a scale diagram to work out the component of the weight that acts along the ramp (see diagram on the right).

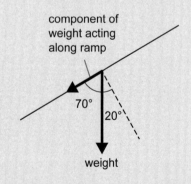

c. The force needed to keep the suitcase moving up the ramp is the same size as the force you have just calculated along the ramp. Use this force to calculate the work done when the person moves the suitcase onto the platform by pushing it up the ramp.

_____

d. Compare your answers to parts **a** and **c** and comment on any differences.

_____

_____

_____

1. a. Which positively charged particles are found in the **nucleus** of an **atom**? _____

b. Which other particles with a similar mass are found in the nucleus? _____

c. What electric charge do the particles in your answer to part **b** have? _____

2. Draw circuit diagrams for the circuits shown in the diagrams below.

a

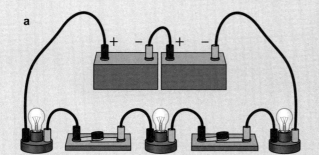

b

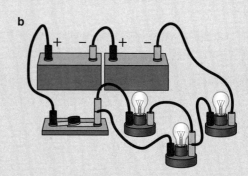

3. Complete the table to compare the differences between **series** and **parallel circuits**.

Series circuits	Parallel circuits

4. In the circuits shown below, all the lamps and cells are the same. Circle the **two** circuits in which the lamps have the same brightness.

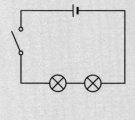 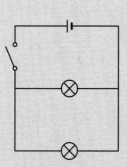 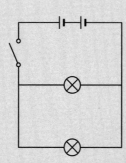 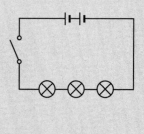 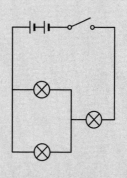

1. A student connects a lamp in a circuit with a **cell** and a switch. She wants to measure the current through the lamp and the **potential difference** across it.

a. Draw a circuit including meters to measure the current and the potential difference.

b. State the name of the meter used to measure current. _____

c. State the name of the meter used to measure potential difference. _____

2. Describe **two** conditions needed to produce an electric current.

_____

_____

3. Define potential difference.

_____

_____

_____

4. In the circuit below, all the lamps are identical.

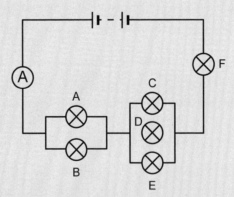

a. Calculate the current passing through each of the lamps A–E when the reading on the **ammeter** is 4.8 A.

_____

b. The potential difference across the single lamp F is 6.6 V. The potential difference across the two lamps A and B in parallel is 3.3 V. The potential difference across the three lamps in parallel C, D and E is 2.2 V. Calculate the total potential difference of the **battery**.

_____

1. Look at this graph of current against potential difference for a filament lamp. Explain how the current changes when the potential difference across the filament lamp is increased.

_____

_____

_____

2. Explain what happens to the current when the potential difference across a fixed resistor is doubled.

_____

_____

3. a. Sketch a graph of current against potential difference for a **diode**.

b. Explain how and why the graph looks different for negative values of potential difference.

_____

_____

_____

_____

c. Explain what happens to the current and the resistance as the potential difference is increased in the positive direction.

_____

_____

d. Give an example of the use of a diode. _____

e. What is a diode that gives out light called? _____

4. A **light-dependent resistor** (LDR) has a resistance of 100 Ω.

a. Calculate the current through the LDR when the potential difference is 5 V. _____

b. You shine a light on the LDR. What will happen to its resistance? _____

c. What will happen to the current in part **b** if the potential difference stays the same? _____

d. Describe a use for an LDR.

_____

5. A **thermistor** is in a circuit with a potential difference of 12 V. The current is 3 A.

a. What is the resistance of the thermistor? _____

b. The circuit is put in a freezer.
What will happen to the resistance of the thermistor? _____

c. What will happen to the current in part **b** if the potential difference stays the same? _____

d. Describe a use of a thermistor. _____

Use mains voltage = 230 V for questions about appliances that use mains electricity.

1. a. What are the units and symbol for **power**? _____

b. Describe what is meant by power.

_____

_____

2. Write down the equation relating power to energy transfer.

3. If the energy transfer is not known, write down **two** other equations that may be used to calculate the power transfer in an electric circuit.

_____

4. Calculate the following:

a. the energy transferred in a 400 W food blender that is switched on for 2 minutes

_____

b. the power of a mains washing machine that takes a current of 2.2 A

_____

c. the current in a 1.4 kW mains coffee maker.

_____

5. A shopper has the choice of buying a 3 kW fast boil kettle or a 1.8 kW kettle. Both use mains electricity. The 3 kW kettle takes 5 minutes to boil some water. How long will the 1.8 kW kettle take to boil the same amount of water? Assume that the energy transferred heating the kettle and surroundings is the same and can be ignored.

_____

6. An electric bicycle has a 36 V battery for a motor that transfers 78 000 J of energy in 5 minutes. Calculate:

a. the power of the motor

_____

b. the current in the motor circuit

_____

c. the electrical resistance of the motor circuit.

_____

Edexcel GCSE (9-1)

Sciences
Homework & skills

CP9h Transferring energy by electricity

CP9 Electricity
and Circuits

1. When energy is transferred by electricity, it is transferred from an energy store. State the energy store at the start, when:

a. an electrical appliance is connected to a battery. _____

b. an electrical appliance is connected by the **mains** supply
to a generator spinning at the power station. _____

c. an electrical appliance is connected to a dynamo that is spinning. _____

2. When we use electricity, in most cases the energy is transferred to something that is meant to heat up or to move. Which of the following have only a heating device, which have only a motor and which have both?

a. battery-operated electric blanket   heating / motor / both

b. mains-operated sewing machine   heating / motor / both

c. battery-operated screwdriver   heating / motor / both

d. mains-operated curling tongs   heating / motor / both

e. mains-operated filament lamp (*Hint:* what makes it give out light?)   heating / motor / both

f. mains-operated fan heater   heating / motor / both

3. What is the energy store that is increased when energy is transferred by:

a. a motor _____

b. a heating device? _____

4. State an advantage of using batteries rather than mains electricity for a laptop.

_____

5. Why would you use mains electricity and not a battery for a power shower?

_____

6. State how the energy transferred depends on the power rating of an appliance.

_____

7. If appliance A has double the power rating of appliance B and they are on for the same amount of time, how does the energy transferred compare?

_____

8. Calculate:

a. the energy transferred by a 3 kW kettle in 15 minutes

_____

b. the energy transferred by a 2.5 kW oven in 1 hour. Give your answer in standard form.

_____

Edexcel GCSE (9-1)

Sciences
Homework & skills

CP10a Magnets and magnetic fields

CP10 Magnetism and
the Motor Effect

1. Describe **two** ways in which you can arrange a pair of bar magnets so that they will repel each other.

2. You can pick up a number of paper clips using a bar magnet. Explain how this demonstrates **permanent** and **induced magnetism**.

3. **a.** Describe **three** ways in which magnets can be used in a kitchen.

b. List **three** pieces of electrical equipment that include magnets.

4. Explain how to use **plotting compasses** to find the shape of the **magnetic field** of a bar magnet.

5. **a.** Draw a bar magnet and sketch the shape of the magnetic field around it. Include arrows to show the direction of the field.

b. Explain how your drawing shows where the magnetic field is strongest.

Sciences
CP10c Magnetic forces
Homework & skills

H 1. Describe **Fleming's left-hand rule** and what it is used for.

_____

_____

_____

_____

_____

_____

H 2. Look at diagram A. Explain the directions of the forces on the wire and on the magnet, and compare their sizes.

_____

_____

_____

_____

_____

_____

_____

Diagram A

H 3. Explain the size and direction of the force produced when the circuit is placed near a magnetic field, as shown in diagram B.

_____

_____

_____

_____

_____

_____

Diagram B

The equation $F = B \times I \times l$ links the force on a wire to **magnetic flux density**, current and the length of the wire.

H 4. Calculate the force on a 2 m long wire at right angles to a magnetic field with a flux density of 0.05 N/A m. The current in the wire is 0.02 A.

_____

H 5. Find **two** different combinations of current and wire length that will produce a force of 2 N on a wire in a magnetic field with a flux density of 0.5 N/A m.

_____

_____

1. a. Explain why the voltage of the electricity produced by power stations is increased before it is transmitted through the **national grid**.

_____

_____

b. What is used to change the voltage? _____

c. Why is the voltage decreased again before electricity is supplied to homes?

_____

_____

2. This diagram represents the national grid. Label:

a. the **step-down** and **step-up** transformers

b. the voltages in the different parts of the grid.

3. Some energy is always transferred to the surroundings when a current flows through a wire.

a. How is this energy transferred? _____

b. Is this energy always wasted energy? Explain your answer.

_____

_____

H 4. You can induce an electric current in a wire by moving a magnet relative to the coil.

a. Describe **two** different ways in which you can increase the size of the induced current.

_____

_____

b. Describe how you can reverse the direction of the induced current.

_____

_____

H 5. Explain how a transformer works.

_____

_____

_____

_____

CP12a Particles and density

1. Diagrams A–E show a substance in different states.

Write the letters of the diagrams in order to show what happens when a gas is cooled to a liquid and then a solid.

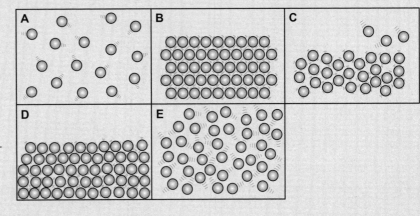

_____

2. a. How do diagrams B and D show that solids and liquids are incompressible?

_____

_____

b. What property (or properties) do liquids and gases have in common?

_____

 3. Ice floats on water because it is less dense than water. Explain why this is unusual, in as much detail as you can. Use ideas about particles in your answer.

_____

_____

_____

_____

_____

4. a. Why is a **change of state** referred to as a **physical change**?

_____

b. What is **conserved** in both physical and **chemical changes**?

_____

 5. A block of concrete has a mass of 800 kg. Its volume is 0.6 m³. Calculate the **density** of the concrete. Give your answer to an appropriate number of significant figures.

_____

 6. The density of sandstone is 2200 kg/m³. A statue made out of sandstone has a volume of 2 m³. Calculate the mass of the statue.

_____

Use these equations to help you answer the questions.

change in thermal energy (J) = mass (kg) × specific heat capacity (J/kg °C) × change in temperature (°C)

thermal energy needed for a change of state (J) = mass (kg) × specific latent heat (J/kg)

change in gravitational potential energy (J) = mass (kg) × g × change in vertical height (m) (g = 10 N/kg)

1. Some students are investigating the specific heat capacity of lead shot. They put 0.5 kg of lead shot into a tube and seal the ends with rubber bungs. When the tube is sealed, the distance between the inner sides of the bungs is 1.2 m.

The students hold the tube vertically and then turn it upside down so that the lead shot falls down the tube. As the lead shot falls, its gravitational potential energy (GPE) is transferred to thermal energy.

a. Calculate the amount of energy transferred to thermal energy in the lead shot as it falls down the tube.

_____

b. The students invert the tube 20 times. Calculate the total amount of GPE transferred to thermal energy.

_____

c. The temperature of the lead shot increased by 1.5 °C. Calculate the specific heat capacity of lead.

_____

d. Reference books give the specific heat capacity of lead as 130 J/kg °C. Explain why your answer to part **c** is not the same as this value.

_____

_____

_____

_____

_____

2. Land and sea breezes occur when the sea and the land warm up at different rates during the day. Heating occurs because the Sun transfers 1400 W of power to each square metre on a sunny day. (1 W = 1 J/s)

Material	Specific heat capacity
sand	835 J/kg °C
water	4182 J/kg °C

a. Calculate the temperature change of a square metre of sand and a square metre of water over an hour on a sunny day. Assume the mass of the substance is 100 kg in each case.

_____

b. State any assumptions you made in your calculation in part **a.**

_____

_____

Sciences   **CP12d** Gas temperature and pressure
Homework & skills

1. Fred takes two empty lemonade bottles and puts the tops on firmly. He puts one in an oven at 40 °C (this is not hot enough to melt the plastic bottle). Half an hour later he inspects the bottles and tries to squeeze them in his hands.

a. Explain what Fred will find when he tries to squeeze the two bottles.

_____

b. Explain your answer to part **a** in terms of the movement of particles.

_____

_____

_____

 2. a. Describe what is meant by **absolute zero**.

_____

b. How can the temperature of absolute zero be found experimentally?

_____

_____

_____

_____

3. Two students are talking about temperatures and particles.

i

> The **kinetic energy** of particles in a gas doubles if the temperature doubles.

ii

> If you heat a gas from 30 °C to 60 °C, the kinetic energy of the particles will double.

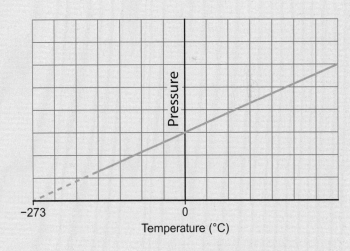

a. Which student is incorrect? Explain your answer.

_____

_____

b. Explain how the other student should change their statement to make sure it is always correct.

_____

_____

_____

1. The table on the right shows the results of an investigation into the **extension** of an object when different forces are applied.

a. Calculate the extension of the object for each force and write them in the correct spaces in the table.

b. Using the graph paper on the next page, plot the points on a graph. Put extension on the horizontal axis and force on the vertical axis.

c. Join the points with a smooth curve.

Force (N)	Length (cm)	Extension (cm)
0	5.0	
5	5.5	
10	7.0	
15	9.0	
20	11.0	
25	12.0	
30	12.5	

2. Explain how you can tell from the graph that the object being tested is a rubber band, not a spring.

_____

_____

_____

3. Draw **two** labelled lines on the graph to represent the results of:

a. stretching a spring that shows a **directly proportional** relationship for all the forces applied to it

b. stretching a spring that starts to behave in a non-linear way for forces above 25 N.

_____

_____

4. Describe the difference between **elastic** and **inelastic** objects.

_____

_____

_____

5. All objects will behave inelastically if the forces on them are large enough. Some uses of materials depend on the material behaving elastically with smaller forces, and some rely on them behaving inelastically even with small forces.

Explain whether each of the following materials is intended to behave elastically or inelastically, and how this property of the material is useful.

a. rubber bands

_____

_____

b. clay used to make pottery

_____

_____

117

You need to use this equation to answer some of the questions.

energy transferred in stretching = ½ × **spring constant** × (extension)^2

1. What does the spring constant of a spring tell you about the spring?

_____

2. Write down the equation that you can use to work out the spring constant.

3. A spring has a spring constant of 35 N/m and a length of 10 cm.

a. Calculate the force needed to give the spring an extension of 20 cm.

_____

b. Calculate the length of the spring with a force of 2 N on it.

_____

4. Calculate the energy transferred when the spring in question **3** is stretched by 80 cm.

_____

5. A spring is stretched using 300 J of energy. The extension is 30 cm. Calculate the spring constant.

_____

6. The graph on the right shows force and extension for a spring.

a. Use information from the graph to work out the spring constant.

_____

b. The spring is stretched using 40 J of energy. Calculate the extension.

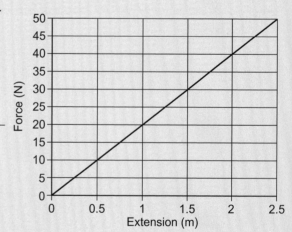

_____

Work done is the energy transferred when a force moves through a distance. The formula for calculating work done is:

work done (J) = force (N) × distance moved in direction of force (m)

7. Calculate the work done when a force of 20 N moves through a distance of 50 cm.

_____

CP1 Motion
CP1a Vectors and scalars

The following things can all be measured in physics. Explain which of these are vectors and which are scalars.

a. acceleration _____

b. volume _____

c. friction _____

d. area _____

CP2 Forces and Motion
CP2b Newton's First Law

Ⓗ Some racing tracks for cars or bicycles have banked corners – this is where the road surface is sloped inwards going around a bend.

Use ideas about friction and **centripetal force** to explain why the banked corners allow the racers to go faster. If you wish, you can include a diagram to help your explanation.

(*Hint*: remember that when you are standing on the ground, your weight does not make you accelerate downwards because there is a balancing upwards force from the ground, and a faster or sharper turn needs a greater centripetal force).

_____

_____

_____

_____

_____

CP2d Newton's Second Law

Ⓗ Formula 1® racing cars must have a mass at or above a certain limit. The rules have been introduced for safety reasons. Explain why a lower mass car might be safer when driving fast around corners. Use the words centripetal force and friction in your answer.

_____

_____

_____

_____

_____

_____

_____

_____

_____

_____

_____

CP2f Momentum

H When a lump of clay is dropped through a vertical height and lands on the ground, it does not bounce. Before hitting the ground, it has momentum. Once it hits the ground, it has no momentum because its velocity is zero. How can it be true that in this collision momentum has been conserved?

_____

_____

_____

_____

_____

_____

_____

_____

_____

_____

_____

_____

_____

_____

CP3 Conservation of Energy

CP3b Energy efficiency

A fridge is standing in the middle of an empty room with all the doors and windows closed. The fridge is switched on and its door is opened.

a. Will the temperature in the room go down, stay the same or go up?

_____

b. Explain your answer to part **a**.

_____

_____

_____

_____

_____

CP4 Waves

CP4b Wave speeds

In 1969 the Apollo astronauts left a laser reflector on the Moon. This was to be used to help scientists to make very accurate measurements of the distance between the Earth and the Moon. The mean distance between the centres of the Earth and Moon is 385 000 km, and light travels at 3×10^8 m/s.

a. How long would it take a beam of light to travel between the centres of the Earth and Moon?

_____

_____

b. The diameter of the Earth is 12 742 km and the diameter of the Moon is 3480 km. How long would it be before the reflection of a laser beam fired from Earth was detected on the Earth? State any assumptions you make in working out your answer.

_____

_____

_____

CP4c **Refraction**

H One type of mirage occurs because light from the sky is refracted so that when it reaches our eyes it appears to be coming from the ground, as shown in the diagram below.

This usually happens on hot days, when the ground is hot and heats the layer of air above it.

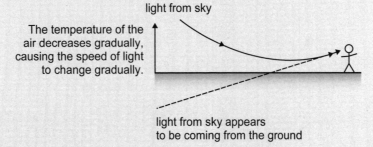

light from sky

The temperature of the air decreases gradually, causing the speed of light to change gradually.

light from sky appears to be coming from the ground

a. Explain how this shows that light travels faster in warm air than in cold air.

_____

_____

_____

b. A 'superior mirage' occurs when objects appear to float in the sky. This occurs when there is a layer of warm air above a layer of cold air. Draw a diagram similar to the one above to show why this happens.

CP5 Light and the Electromagnetic Spectrum
CP5b **The electromagnetic spectrum**

Light travels at around 2×10^8 m/s in glass. The frequency of light is 3×10^{14} Hz. When light enters a glass block its frequency does not change. Calculate the wavelength of visible light in glass.

_____

CP5c Using the long wavelengths

H 'All the wavelengths from visible light to radio waves are reflected by metals'. Give examples to show that this statement could be correct.

_____

_____

_____

_____

_____

_____

_____

_____

_____

CP5d Using the short wavelengths

Find out what a barium meal is and how it is used in hospitals together with X-rays to investigate problems in the digestive system.

_____

_____

_____

_____

_____

_____

_____

_____

CP6 Radioactivity

You will need a copy of the periodic table to help you answer some of these questions.

CP6a Atomic models

Dalton's model of atoms as spheres is still used to explain observations such as substances expanding when they are heated. Suggest why this model is still used even though we now have more detailed atomic models.

_____

_____

_____

_____

_____

CP6f **Radioactive decay**

Different elements can form when a nucleus absorbs an alpha particle or a beta particle. Write a nuclear equation to show what happens when nitrogen-14 is:

a. struck by an alpha particle to form oxygen-17 and hydrogen

_____

b. struck by a neutron from cosmic radiation to form carbon-14. (*Hint:* another atom is formed as well.)

_____

CP7 Energy – Forces Doing Work
CP7a **Work and power**

The world's fastest lifts are in the Shanghai Tower in China. They move at up to 18 m/s. Until recently, the lifts in the Taipei 101 building in Taiwan were the fastest, with a top speed of 16.8 m/s. However, the speed of a lift does not necessarily tell you how powerful it is.

a. Explain why someone might think that the fastest lift is also the most powerful.

_____

_____

b. Explain what you need to know to work out which of these two lifts is the more powerful.

_____

_____

_____

CP8 Forces and their Effects
CP8b **Vector diagrams**

H An aeroplane is approaching a runway. Its engines are producing 40 kN of thrust. The wind is pushing the aeroplane at right angles to the runway with a force of 10 kN. Calculate the angle to the runway at which the aeroplane must point if it is to land safely.

_____

CP9 Electricity and Circuits
CP9a **Electric circuits**

a. What is an electric current?

_____

b. Compare conventional current with **electron** flow.

_____

_____

_____

CP9b Current and potential difference

Look at the circuit diagram opposite.

Calculate:

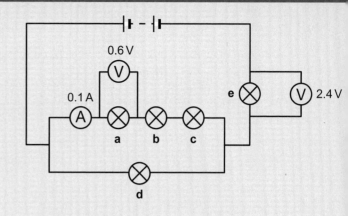

a. the current in each lamp

_____

b. the potential difference across each lamp

_____

c. the potential difference supplied by the battery.

_____

CP9e More about resistance

A **light-emitting diode** (LED) has very low resistance when the potential difference across it is higher than 2 V.

a. i If the potential difference across a diode is greater than 2 V what will happen to the current through it?

_____

ii Suggest what effect this may have on the LED.

_____

b. Suggest why a LED usually has a fixed resistor connected in series with it.

_____

c. This series circuit has a 5 V battery and a fixed resistor in series with the LED. Calculate the value of resistance needed to make sure the potential difference across the LED is not greater than 2 V and the current through it is not greater than 10 mA.

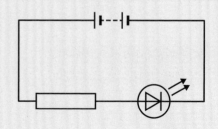

_____

d. If this value of resistor is not available, explain whether a resistor with a higher or a lower value should be used.

_____

CP9g **Power**

3 kW of electrical power is transmitted across the country on the overhead power lines of the 400 kV 'supergrid' and then using the 230 V mains system.

a. Calculate the current required to deliver this power in the 400 kV cables and the 230 V cables.

_____

b. Compare the power transferred in heating a cable with a resistance of 10 Ω when the power is transmitted at 400 kV and when it is transmitted at 230 V.

_____

CP10 Magnetism and the Motor Effect

CP10a **Magnets and magnetic fields**

Ordnance Survey maps mark three directions as north: true north, magnetic north and grid north.

Find out and explain what the differences are between these three directions.

_____
_____
_____
_____
_____
_____
_____
_____
_____

CP10c **Magnetic forces**

 H A wire is not always at right angles to the magnetic field. A more general form of the equation for the force on a wire is:

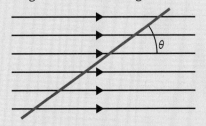

$$F = B \times I \times l \times \sin\theta$$

where θ (the Greek letter theta) is the angle between the wire and the magnetic field.

a. Find the value of $\sin\theta$ when $\theta = 90°$.

b. Explain why the formula here is the same as the formula given on page 111 when the wire is at right angles to the magnetic field.

CP11 Electromagnetic Induction
CP11b **Transformers and energy**

The output of a transformer is **alternating current**. Many electrical devices require a supply of direct current. Explain how a diode could be used to convert a.c. to d.c., and suggest one disadvantage of this.

CP12 Particle Model
CP12d **Gas temperature and pressure**

A teacher takes an empty metal oil can and puts a little water in it. She heats the can until the water starts to form steam and then screws the cap on and removes the can from the heat. After a few minutes the can suddenly crumples up. Explain why this happens in as much detail as you can.

CP13 Forces and Matter

CP13a **Bending and stretching**

 The diagram below shows six sets of springs. All the springs are identical, and the same mass is hanging on the bottom of each set of springs. Explain how far each of arrangements B–F would stretch compared with the single spring in A.

_____

_____

_____

_____

_____

_____

_____

_____

_____

_____

_____

_____

_____

_____

_____

_____

_____

_____

Recall and apply:

distance travelled = average speed × time	
acceleration = $\dfrac{\text{change in velocity}}{\text{time taken}}$	$a = \dfrac{(v - u)}{t}$
force = mass × acceleration	$F = m \times a$
weight = mass × gravitational field strength	$W = m \times g$
efficiency = $\dfrac{\text{(useful energy transferred by the device)}}{\text{(total energy supplied to the device)}}$	
H **momentum = mass × velocity**	$p = m \times v$
wave speed = frequency × wavelength	$v = f \times \lambda$
wave speed = distance ÷ time	$v = \dfrac{x}{t}$
density = mass ÷ volume	$\rho = \dfrac{m}{V}$
work done = force × distance moved in direction of force	$E = F \times d$
change in gravitational potential energy = mass × gravitational field strength × change in vertical height	$\Delta GPE = m \times g \times \Delta h$
kinetic enegy = ½ × mass × (speed)²	$KE = \frac{1}{2} \times m \times v^2$
power = work done ÷ time taken	$P = \dfrac{E}{t}$
energy transferred = charge moved × potential difference	$E = Q \times V$
charge = current × time	$Q = I \times t$
potential difference = current × resistance	$V = I \times R$
power = energy transferred ÷ time taken	$P = \dfrac{E}{t}$
electrical power = current × potential difference	$P = I \times V$
electrical power = (current)² × resistance	$P = I^2 \times R$
force exerted on a spring = spring constant × extension	$F = k \times x$

Select and apply:

(final velocity)² – (initial velocity)² = 2 × acceleration × distance	$v^2 - u^2 = 2 \times a \times x$
H **force = change in momentum ÷ time**	$F = \dfrac{(mv - mu)}{t}$
energy transferred = current × potential difference × time	$E = I \times V \times t$
H **force on a conductor at right angles to a magnetic field carrying a current = magnetic flux density × current × length**	$F = B \times I \times l$
For transformers with 100% efficiency, potential difference across primary coil × current in primary coil = potential difference across secondary coil × current in secondary coil	$V_p \times I_p = V_s \times I_s$
change in thermal energy = mass × specific heat capacity × change in temperature	$\Delta Q = m \times c \times \Delta\theta$
thermal energy for a change of state = mass × specific latent heat	$Q = m \times L$
energy transferred in stretching = 0.5 × spring constant × (extension)²	$E = \frac{1}{2} \times k \times x^2$